THE HEART OF THE ATOM

BERNARD L. COHEN is director of the Scaife Nuclear Laboratories at the University of Pittsburgh in Pennsylvania. A graduate of the Case Institute of Technology, he received the M.S. degree from the University of Pittsburgh and the D.Sc. degree from the Carnegie Institute of Technology. Dr. Cohen has worked at the Oak Ridge National Laboratory, where he led a team doing research on the Oak Ridge 86-inch cyclotron.

Dr. Cohen has contributed to scientific journals numerous articles on various aspects of nuclear physics. His decision to write this book grew out of a realization that while our understanding of the structure of the nucleus is about as thorough as that of atomic structure, popular presentations of the nucleus are practically nonexistent. THE HEART OF THE ATOM is one of Dr. Cohen's steps to remedy that situation. He has also given series of talks on nuclear structure at many high schools and colleges, and published a paper on the subject in *International Science and Technology*.

Bernard L. Cohen

·

THE HEART OF
THE ATOM

THE STRUCTURE OF THE ATOMIC NUCLEUS

Published by Anchor Books
Doubleday & Company, Inc.
Garden City, New York
1967

THE SCIENCE STUDY SERIES

The Science Study Series offers to students and to the general public the writing of distinguished authors on the most stirring and fundamental topics of science, from the smallest known particles to the whole universe. Some of the books tell of the role of science in the world of man, his technology and civilization. Others are biographical in nature, telling the fascinating stories of the great discoverers and their discoveries. All the authors have been selected both for expertness in the fields they discuss and for ability to communicate their special knowledge and their own views in an interesting way. The primary purpose of these books is to provide a survey within the grasp of the young student or the layman. Many of the books, it is hoped, will encourage the reader to make his own investigations of natural phenomena.

The Series, which now offers topics in all the sciences and their applications, had its beginning in a project to revise the secondary schools' physics curriculum. At the Massachusetts Institute of Technology during 1956 a group of physicists, high school teachers, journalists, apparatus designers, film producers, and other specialists organized the Physical Science Study Committee, now operating as a part of Educational Services Incorporated, Watertown, Massachusetts. They pooled their knowledge and experience toward the design and creation of aids to the learning of physics. Initially their effort was supported by the National Science Foundation, which has continued to aid the program. The Ford Foundation, the Fund for the Advancement of Education, and the Alfred P. Sloan Foundation have also given support. The Committee has created a textbook, an extensive film series, a laboratory guide, specially designed apparatus, and a teachers' source book.

The Series is guided by a Board of Editors consisting of Bruce F. Kingsbury, Managing Editor; John H. Durston, General Editor; Paul F. Brandwein, the Conservation Foundation, and Harcourt, Brace & World, Inc.; Samuel A. Goudsmit, Brookhaven National Laboratory; Philippe LeCorbeiller, Harvard University; and Gerard Piel, *Scientific American*.

PROLOGUE

It would be a poor bookstore nowadays that did not offer the general reader at least one book, hardbound or paperback, about the atom. *Atoms in Action, The Restless Atom, The World of the Atom**—these and similar titles on store shelves and in reading lists for high school pupils bear witness to the great importance of the atom in our lives, and attest the popular interest. In the past twenty years the atom has entered the public market place.

The ancient Greek philosophers talked about "atoms," but they would feel more at home today among students of the calculus than in a research lab. The wonderful science of chemistry, as we know it, grew from the laboriously accumulated, empirical knowledge of metalworkers and from the secret (and often illegal) experiments of the alchemists, not from philosophic discourse on infinitesimals, and it is this science that has brought the detailed properties of atoms into focus. Chemists discovered and named the hundred or so different types of atoms in our universe, and learned how atoms combine and break apart. With

* G. Harrison, *Atoms in Action*, 3rd edition. Verry Press, 1965.

Alfred Romer, *The Restless Atom*. Science Study Series No. S12. Doubleday & Co., Inc., 1960.

H. Boorse, *The World of the Atom*. Basic Books, 1966.

this understanding, they have combined atoms in millions of different ways to produce all the wondrous substances that have contributed to our material comforts—"better things for better living," as one advertising slogan puts it. At the same time, the chemists have probed into the combinations of atoms that form the molecules of organic cells, and they seem to be approaching the threshold of creating life itself.

But scientists were not satisfied with learning *how* atoms combine and separate; they also wanted to know *why*. In the last century, when experiments with the passage of electric current through solutions and through gases in partially evacuated tubes revealed new phenomena and gave new insights into already known phenomena, chemists and physicists began to study and to speculate upon the structure of the atom. They concluded, early in this century, that the atom consisted of a tiny but massive *nucleus* surrounded by very light *electrons*, the latter orbiting much as the planets orbit the Sun. In this picture, electrical forces —the attraction between positively charged nucleus and negatively charged electrons—hold the atom together.

The electrons turned out to be most interesting. It is their behavior that determines the chemical properties of atoms—why wood burns but rocks do not, why food sustains life when combined with the air we breathe, why salt dissolves in water, why antiseptics kill germs. The electrons also determine the physical properties of the molecules and crystals into which atoms combine: why steel is strong and rigid, but oil flows and is slippery; why metals conduct electricity, but other substances ordinarily do not; why some materials boil at hundreds of degrees below zero while others remain solid at blast-furnace temperatures. There is scarcely a question one can ask about the behavior of matter here on Earth that cannot be answered in terms of the orbiting electrons.

One might wonder what, beyond its comparatively great weight, is left to the nucleus, the heart of the atom. The nucleus does, of course, hold the electrons in orbit by the electrical forces it exerts on them, but is this its only function? Or has it a more direct effect on our daily lives?

One illustration of the immediate importance of the nucleus came very dramatically to public attention in August of 1945 in a blinding flash over Hiroshima, Japan; the tremendous power released by interacting atomic nuclei had completely revolutionized human warfare. It was at once clear that this power could also be harnessed for peaceful uses. Now, about twenty years later, it is supplying a significant fraction of the world's energy requirements, and in another century or so it will have to supply practically all to keep our technology-based society moving in high gear. In the process, application of nuclear power to desalt ocean water probably will solve the world's increasingly difficult water problems. The "ashes" left in these processes of energy production emit radiations which are being used for extraordinary advances in medicine, engineering, chemistry, biology, etc.

But while these nuclear effects arranged by man are indeed earth-shaking, the cosmic significance of the heart of the atom is to be seen only out beyond the Earth, in the stars. There, nuclei in collision provide the energy which stars, such as our Sun, radiate. This radiation, as we well know, is the ultimate source of all energy in the universe. How unthinkable would be a universe without it—dark, cold, lifeless! Moreover, it is in these collisions between nuclei that the various types of atoms discovered by the chemists were formed, and are still being formed. It may well be said that the nucleus is the ultimate source of virtually all matter and energy in the universe.

In this book we will try to describe all aspects of the atomic nucleus. We will start with the inside of a nucleus, to see how it is put together. This is an aspect usually ignored in popular books, and in fact it is only in the last decade that scientists themselves have succeeded in comprehending the structure. We will see how the neutrons and protons of nuclei move around, and what happens when they bump into one another. Building on this understanding, we will see how and why nuclei emit various types of radiation and interact with one another. When we have achieved some understanding of these small-scale aspects of the nucleus, we will shift our attention to large-scale applications of nuclear phenomena here on earth—the effects and uses of radiations, and the methods of deriving the energy we need to power our civilization (or, God forbid, to destroy it). Finally, we will explain how nuclear collisions provide the fantastic amounts of energy produced in stars, how they alter the structure of stars, and how these processes led to formation of the various kinds of atoms of which our universe is composed.

CONTENTS

CHAPTER I

THE STRUCTURE OF THE NUCLEUS— DEFINING THE PROBLEM

It is well known that an atom is somewhat like a miniature solar system, having a small but very massive nucleus at the center surrounded by orbiting electrons. Models of atoms detailing the orbits of the electrons are on display in planetariums and at high school science fairs; even elementary school science classes discuss the orbiting electrons. The nucleus, on the other hand, is depicted usually as a structureless ball at the center, and the vague impression given is that of an inert lump of some kind. Actually, there is no reasonable justification for this preferential treatment of electrons. The structure of the nucleus is no less well understood than is the electronic structure of atoms.

The nucleus consists of two types of particles, *neutrons* and *protons*. We speak of them collectively as *nucleons*. The protons carry a positive electrical charge, and since the atom as a unit is electrically neutral, the number of protons in the nucleus is just equal to the number of orbiting electrons in the atom. This is familiar to chemistry students as the *atomic number*. Oxygen, for example, has atomic number 8: its nucleus contains eight protons. Since the nucleus contains virtually all the mass of the atom, the *atomic weight* is just the total number of nucleons in the nucleus. Thus, the oxygen nucleus of atomic weight 16, which is called oxygen-16, must contain eight neutrons in addition to its eight protons, and similarly the nucleus of oxygen-17 must consist of eight protons and nine neutrons. We designate a nucleus by a row of three boxes displaying, respectively, the number of protons, the number of neutrons, and the chemical symbol followed by the atomic weight. Thus, oxygen-17 is designated $\boxed{8\mid 9\mid \text{O-17}}$. For another example, the common aluminum isotope, aluminum-27, is designated $\boxed{13\mid 14\mid \text{Al-27}}$, indicating that its nucleus consists of thirteen protons and fourteen neutrons. Actually, these designations are redundant; once we know the number of protons and neutrons, we can tell the name of the element (from the number of protons) and the atomic weight (from the sum of the two). We retain the last box only as a convenience for those acquainted with the notation. Readers who have not studied chemistry can ignore it; the number of protons and neutrons is all they need to know. (A list of the chemical elements, their symbols, and their atomic number—i.e., the number of protons they contain—is given in the Appendix.)

How are these neutrons and protons arranged in the nucleus? How do they move about? Do they bump into one another, and what happens if they do? The answers to these questions constitute the "structure of the nucleus." Please note the wording of this last sentence; its significance will appear in due course.

It is an unfortunate fact of nature that systems such as atoms and their nuclei are governed by the laws of *quantum physics*, which are different from the physical laws we encounter in everyday life. For example, it is natural to think of an electron as a particle having all the properties of a ball, except that it is very much smaller. In quantum physics, however, a particle has many properties that are not consistent with this picture and are therefore difficult to comprehend. For example, it is not possible, even in principle, to know accurately where the particle is located or in what direction it is moving. These are properties we would never associate with a ball, no matter how small.

We must therefore face the difficult situation that while scientists can understand nuclear structure and the electronic structure of atoms under the laws of quantum physics, an understanding of these laws requires a background in mathematics and physics far beyond that of any but specialists. The only reasonable procedure, therefore, is to make a *translation* from the world of quantum physics to the physics of the everyday world in which particles do behave like balls. As we might expect, something is lost in translation, but a great deal does come through. In any case, the translation we will follow in explaining nuclear structure is the same as that widely used in explaining the structure of electrons in atoms. Anyone willing to accept the models of atoms found in planetariums need have no compunction about accepting the model of the nucleus that we present here. Most of the loss occurs at the outset, since we will have to begin by stating a series of facts for which we can offer no explanation except to say that they arise very naturally from the laws of quantum physics. But once these facts are accepted, the rest of the story follows in a relatively simple and logical fashion. With this reward in prospect, perhaps the reader will bear with us.

CHAPTER II

ALLOWED ORBITS

Neutrons and protons, as we have said, are queer to our everyday world in that they must live by the rules of quantum physics. Perhaps solace is to be found in the fact that their neighbors in the atom, the electrons, also have to follow these laws. Be that as it may, here are the rules.

The first law is that nucleons can move only in certain "allowed" orbits. These orbits are specified by four identifying tags known as *quantum numbers;* a statement of the four quantum numbers for an orbit gives its complete description. Moreover, these quantum numbers can have only certain particular values; hence, unlike the situation of planets and satellites, only certain very specific orbits are allowed. The four quantum numbers, their allowed values, and their physical significance are listed in Table I.

As Table I shows, the n quantum number determines the energy of the nucleon in the orbit. For most purposes, this is another way of saying that the energy of the nucleon depends on the speed with which it travels around in the nucleus; a higher speed means a greater energy and hence a larger value of n.

The l quantum number determines the shape of the orbit. Higher l orbits are more circular and lower l orbits more elliptical. An $l = 0$ orbit is the extreme case of an ellipse, a simple vibration along a straight line back and forth through the center of the nucleus.

The j quantum number determines whether the orbital motion of the nucleon is in the same direction as,

TABLE I

The Quantum Numbers That Specify Allowed Orbits

Quantum number	Physical Significance	Allowed values
n	energy of nucleon in orbit	$1, 2, 3, 4, \ldots$
l	shape of orbit ◯ ⬭ ⬮ $\cdots$ | $n-1$ $n-3$ $n-5$ 0	$(n-1), (n-3), (n-5),$ $\ldots 1$ or 0
j	$j = (l + \frac{1}{2})$ $j = (l - \frac{1}{2})$	$(l + \frac{1}{2}),\ (l - \frac{1}{2})$
m	orientation of orbit in space	$j, (j-1), (j-2),$ $--- (-j)$

or in the opposite direction from, its "spin." (Nucleons, as well as electrons, have a spin, just as the Earth spins on its axis. The Earth goes around once per day, but nucleons spin around some 30 billion trillion times per second.)

The m quantum number gives the orientation of the orbit in space; it tells whether the orbit is horizontal, vertical, or tilted in some direction. A student of geometry might object here that it is impossible to specify a direction in space by one quantity. For example, the direction of a star in the heavens is specified by two angles, the azimuth and declination. We won't argue with him. This is one of the matters lost in the translation from quantum physics. While the value of m does not specify completely the orientation of the orbit in space, it gives all the information possible under the laws of quantum physics. For convenience of discussion, we will accept the proposition that a specification of the quantum numbers (n, l, j, m) describes an orbit completely. The situation for electrons in atoms is analogous.

By making use of all the allowed values for the quantum numbers listed in Table I, we can make a complete list of allowed orbits. The beginning of such a list is shown in Table II, and an explanation of how they are obtained is given in the caption. For the reader who is interested in the results rather than in the method of obtaining them only the first and last rows of Table II are important. Those rows give the number of allowed orbits for each value of n—two allowed for $n = 1$, six for $n = 2$, twelve for $n = 3$, etc.

The reason why this relationship is important is that the energy of a particle in an orbit depends primarily on the quantum number n. These energies are therefore distributed in groups, as shown in Fig. 1. The two $n = 1$ orbits have the lowest energy, the six $n = 2$ orbits have the next lowest energy, etc. These groupings of orbit energies are called *shells*. The origin of that term is of some interest in our story.

The orbits allowed to *electrons in atoms* also are characterized by four quantum numbers, and there again, the energies are largely determined by the quantum number n. In addition, n determines the average *radius* of the electron orbit. Thus, the electron orbits for a given n have not only the same energy but the same size, and as a consequence they lie in something resembling a spherical *shell*, like a hollow rubber ball. Electron orbits with the next higher value of n have a considerably larger radius; consequently they lie in a *shell* of larger radius. Thus, groups of electron orbits with the same n quantum numbers are called *shells*. In nuclei, on the other hand, it turns out that the radius of the orbits followed by neutrons and

TABLE II

Quantum Numbers of Allowed Orbits in n = 1, 2, *and* 3

(This lists all orbits allowed by the rules of Table I.)

From Table I, the l quantum number can be $n - 1$, $n - 3$, . . . So, for $n = 3$, l can be $(3 - 1) = 2$ or $(3 - 3) = 0$. The j quantum number can be $(l + \frac{1}{2})$ or $(l - \frac{1}{2})$; at $l = 2$, for example, j can be $(2 + \frac{1}{2}) = \frac{5}{2}$ or $(2 - \frac{1}{2}) = \frac{3}{2}$. Note that j must be positive; for $l = 0$, j can only be $\frac{1}{2}$. The m quantum number can be j, $(j - 1)$, $(j - 2)$, etc., down to $(-j)$; when $j = \frac{5}{2}$, for example, m can be $\frac{5}{2}$, $\frac{3}{2}$, $\frac{1}{2}$, $-\frac{1}{2}$, $-\frac{3}{2}$, $-\frac{5}{2}$. Since a specification of the four quantum numbers completely describes the orbit, no two orbits can have all four quantum numbers the same. Therefore, to find the number of orbits with a given n quantum number (as listed in the last row), one must just see how many combinations of (n, l, j, m) can be formed. For $n = 1$, there are just two: $(1, 0, \frac{1}{2}, +\frac{1}{2})$ and $(1, 0, \frac{1}{2}, -\frac{1}{2})$. For $n = 2$, there are six: $(2, 1, \frac{3}{2}, +\frac{3}{2})$, $(2, 1, \frac{3}{2}, +\frac{1}{2})$, $(2, 1, \frac{3}{2}, -\frac{1}{2})$, $(2, 1, \frac{3}{2}, -\frac{3}{2})$, $(2, 1, \frac{1}{2}, +\frac{1}{2})$, and $(2, 1, \frac{1}{2}, -\frac{1}{2})$. For $n = 3$, there are twelve: $(3, 2, \frac{5}{2}, +\frac{5}{2})$, $(3, 2, \frac{5}{2}, +\frac{3}{2})$, etc.

n	1	2		3		
l	0	1		2		0
j	$\frac{1}{2}$	$\frac{3}{2}$	$\frac{1}{2}$	$\frac{5}{2}$	$\frac{3}{2}$	$\frac{1}{2}$
m	$+\frac{1}{2}$ $-\frac{1}{2}$	$+\frac{3}{2}$ $+\frac{1}{2}$ $-\frac{1}{2}$ $-\frac{3}{2}$	$+\frac{1}{2}$ $-\frac{1}{2}$	$+\frac{5}{2}$ $+\frac{3}{2}$ $+\frac{1}{2}$ $-\frac{1}{2}$ $-\frac{3}{2}$ $-\frac{5}{2}$	$+\frac{3}{2}$ $+\frac{1}{2}$ $-\frac{1}{2}$ $-\frac{3}{2}$	$+\frac{1}{2}$ $-\frac{1}{2}$
Number of orbits for each n	2	6		12		

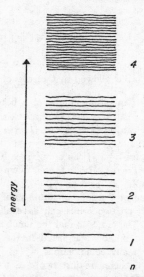

Fig. 1. Energies of the various allowed orbits. Note that the two n = 1 orbits have the lowest energy, the six n = 2 orbits have the next lowest, and so on up the scale.

protons depends only slightly on the quantum number *n*, and all orbits have about the same average radius. Only the *energies* of the nucleons in these orbits occur in groups (as shown in Fig. 1), but nevertheless the term *shell* has been carried over from the groupings of orbit energies of electrons.

We have seen that the first fact of life for a neutron or a proton is that it must move only in an allowed orbit with a speed determined by the *n* quantum number of that orbit; the shape and orientation of the orbit are determined by the *l* and *m* quantum numbers, and the spin by the *j* quantum number. The second fact of life for a nucleon is that it must follow the dictates of the *Pauli exclusion principle*. In atomic physics this principle requires that no more than one electron occupy any orbit. If it were not for this, all electrons would be in the same orbit—the orbit of lowest energy. All the laws of chemistry would be vastly different; solid matter would have completely different properties, if indeed it could exist. The importance of the Pauli exclusion principle for the electrons in atoms would be hard to exaggerate.

In nuclei, this principle has a similar and equally important place, as we shall see. It requires that there can be no more than one proton and no more than one neutron in each allowed orbit. One might get the idea that it is not entirely "exclusive" to allow both a neutron and a proton in each orbit, but actually orbits of neutrons and protons are slightly different even if they have the same quantum numbers.

For reasons we will discuss in Chapter IV, it is normal for a nucleus to be in its state of lowest energy. Thus when a nucleus is in its normal state, the nucleons are in the lowest energy orbits available. The lowest energy orbits are those with $n = 1$, but there are only two available. Therefore, in $\boxed{2\,|\,2\,|\,\text{He-4}}$ (normal helium), which has two neutrons and two protons, all nucleons are in $n = 1$ orbits; but in $\boxed{3\,|\,2\,|\,\text{Li-5}}$, which has two neutrons and three protons, the Pauli exclusion principle requires that one proton be in an $n = 2$ orbit. In the nucleus of ordinary oxygen $\boxed{8\,|\,8\,|\,\text{O-16}}$, which has eight neutrons and eight protons, all nucleons are in $n = 1$ and $n = 2$ orbits, but in $\boxed{8\,|\,9\,|\,\text{O-17}}$ one neutron must be in an $n = 3$ orbit. Nuclei like $\boxed{2\,|\,2\,|\,\text{He-4}}$ and $\boxed{8\,|\,8\,|\,\text{O-16}}$, which have some shells completely filled and all other shells completely empty, are known as "closed shell" nuclei. Nuclei like $\boxed{3\,|\,2\,|\,\text{Li-5}}$ and $\boxed{8\,|\,9\,|\,\text{O-17}}$, which have a single nucleon not in a closed shell, are known as single particle nuclei. These have specially simple properties, and they play roles in nuclear structure analo-

gous to those of the noble gas (closed shell) and alkali
metal (single particle) atoms in atomic structure.

The reader who has some familiarity with the electronic structure of atoms is perhaps impressed at this
point by the strong similarities between atomic and
nuclear structure. It might be useful to pause now for
a more detailed comparison of the two. In size, the
atom is 10,000 times larger, 10^{-8} cm* against 10^{-12} cm.
If the atom were expanded to the size of a large lecture hall, the nucleus would be the size of a pea at
its center. On the other hand, the mass of the nucleus
is about 5000 times larger than that of the electrons
revolving about it. If masses were increased propor-
tionately so that the electrons were as massive as the
air in that lecture hall, the little pea-sized nucleus
would weigh about 100,000 tons. The energies of the
nucleons in the nucleus are very much larger than
those of electrons, typically 10 million eV† against 10
eV, or a million times higher. Some of the quantum
numbers for the two systems are different; even where
they are the same, there are differences in the allowed
values. As a result, the number of orbits in the various

* A centimeter (abbreviated *cm*) is the metric unit of
length. One inch is just over 2½ cm. The symbol 10^{-8}
means the number .00000001, the 1 being in the eighth
decimal place.

† The unit of energy most frequently used in atomic
and nuclear physics is the *electron volt* (abbreviated
eV). An electron with an energy of 1 eV has a velocity
of 370 miles per second, or 1,300,000 miles per hour.
In the filament of an incandescent light bulb, the average
energy of the atoms in their thermal motion is about ¼ eV.
Since the energies in nuclei are very much higher, the
commonly used unit is *million electron volts,* abbreviated
MeV. A 1 MeV neutron or proton moves with a velocity
of 30,000,000 miles per hour.

shells are different. The chemistry student knows that there are eight electrons in the $n = 2$ atomic electron shell, but according to Table II there are only six neutrons or protons in the $n = 2$ nuclear shell.

The orbit radii, as we have seen, differ radically for different n in atoms, but only slightly in nuclei. Further, the energies of orbits in different shells differ much more radically in atoms than in nuclei—by a factor of about 10,000 in a large atom, but only by about a factor of 10 in the largest nuclei.

Perhaps the most spectacular difference is in the force that holds the system together. In the atom this is the electrical attraction between the negatively charged electrons and the positively charged nucleus. However, it is clear that electrical forces cannot hold the nucleus together. Neutrons have no electrical charge and therefore are unaffected by electric forces, and the electrical force between two protons is repulsive since they both have a positive charge. A force of entirely different kind must be holding the nucleus together.* This nuclear or meson force is very strong but acts between two nucleons only when they are close together—say less than 3×10^{-13} cm apart. At greater distances its influence falls off so rapidly that it soon becomes completely negligible. At a trillionth of an inch apart the nucleons ignore each other completely. On the other hand, at distances closer than 5×10^{-14} cm the nuclear force becomes strongly repulsive. Moreover, the Pauli exclusion principle, you will remember, keeps nucleons apart by requiring that they be in different orbits. As a result, the average distance between nucleons in the nucleus is about 1.0×10^{-13} cm.

* A simple quantitative calculation easily shows that gravitational forces can have no significant influence in holding the nucleus together.

The fact that nuclei are held together by the mutual attraction of all the nucleons has a very interesting consequence. Many nuclei take on an ellipsoidal shape, like a long watermelon or a pumpkin, rather than the spherical shape of a basketball. Let us see why this is so.

For a closed shell nucleus such as $\boxed{2 \mid 2 \mid \text{He-4}}$ or $\boxed{8 \mid 8 \mid \text{O-16}}$ orbits of all m values in the filled shells must be occupied, and all orbit orientations in space are equally represented. A closed shell nucleus is therefore spherical. But consider what must happen when nucleons are added to the system. The arriving nucleons must go into orbits in the next higher shell, and since that shell is empty, there is a wide variety of orbits to choose from. Suppose a neutron added to $\boxed{8 \mid 8 \mid \text{O-16}}$ (to give $\boxed{8 \mid 9 \mid \text{O-17}}$) goes into a horizontal orbit. If another neutron is added to give $\boxed{8 \mid 10 \mid \text{O-18}}$, it will also go into a horizontal orbit rather than into an orbit near the vertical plane because the former brings it closer to the attracting first nucleon. Since there are now two nucleons in horizontal orbits, it is even more likely that a third added nucleon will go into a horizontal orbit; two nucleons will now be attracting it to such an orbit. So things continue as more nucleons are added.

But now we must look again at the nucleons in the closed shell orbits (that is, those with $n = 1$ and $n = 2$). It is the combined attraction of all the other nucleons in the nucleus that keeps them in their orbits, but by now a sizable majority of these other nucleons have orbits lying near the horizontal plane. Thus, even the orbits of the nucleons in the closed shells are distorted toward the horizontal plane, and the whole nucleus assumes the shape of an ellipsoid. Typically, the longest axis is about 20 per cent longer than the shortest.

As more nucleons are added, all the orbits near the

horizontal plane become filled. Additional nucleons must either go into orbits lying near the vertical plane, or into horizontal orbits in the next shell. To enter the next shell requires more energy, so the former course is chosen. As still more nucleons are added, they must continue to go into vertical orbits; the nucleus becomes less and less distorted. By the time the shell is filled, all values of m are equally represented and the nucleus is again spherical.

The ellipsoidal nucleus most common to our everyday lives is aluminum, a material used in airplanes, cooking utensils, and innumerable other familiar products. Others are tungsten, of which light-bulb filaments are made, and uranium, the fuel of the atomic age. In general, the nuclei of the neighbors of these three in the periodic table of elements are also deformed.

CHAPTER III

COLLISIONS

We have seen that the activity of nucleons is severely restricted according to the Pauli exclusion principle, which means they are in different orbits. However, these orbits do cross, and one might wonder whether nucleons ever bump into one another. The fact is that they can indeed have collisions, provided certain conditions are fulfilled. These are:

(1) The nucleons after collision must end up in *allowed* and otherwise unoccupied orbits. That is, they must at all times obey the laws of quantum physics, including the Pauli exclusion principle.

(2) *Energy* must be conserved approximately. This is a time-honored law of physics, except that the "approximately" is, as we shall see, a consequence of quantum physics. Since it is the n quantum number principally that determines the energy, this condition requires that the sum of the n quantum numbers of two colliding particles must be the same after the collision as before. For example, if two nucleons with $n = 3$ collide, they can end up in two different $n = 3$ orbits, or one can go onto an $n = 2$ orbit while the other goes into an $n = 4$ orbit; in either event the sum of the n quantum numbers is 6 both before and after the collision. However, the collision cannot result in one nucleon in an $n = 3$ orbit and the other in an $n = 4$ orbit, as that situation would correspond to a change in the sum of the n quantum numbers (from 6 to 7).

(3) *Angular momentum* must be conserved. This, again, is a time-honored law of physics which is widely used, for example in determining orbits of planets and satellites. The conservation of angular momentum is perhaps most familiar in the case of a figure skater doing a spin. He can make himself spin faster or slower by pulling his arms in or out; the property that remains constant (that is, is conserved) is his angular momentum. For a nucleon in a nucleus, the angular momentum and its orientation in space are specified by the j and m quantum numbers respectively. The conservation of angular momentum then requires that the sum of the m quantum numbers be the same after the collision as before, and it puts a more complicated condition on the j quantum numbers which we will not bother to detail here.

(4) *Parity* must be conserved. Parity is a concept with meaning only in quantum physics, but its manifestation here is very simple. Conservation of parity merely requires that if the sum of the l values of the two colliding particles is *even* before the collision, it

must be *even* after; if it is *odd* before the collision, it must be *odd* after. For example, two nucleons in $l = 4$ orbits can collide and end up with one in an $l = 1$ and the other in an $l = 3$ orbit since the sum of the l values was 8 before the collision and 4 after the collision, and both 8 and 4 are even numbers. They cannot, however, end up with one in an $l = 1$ and the other in an $l = 2$ orbit, since the sum of the l values would then be 3, which is odd.

Now let us examine some practical cases to see when these conditions can be satisfied. First, we consider a closed shell nucleus, say $\boxed{8 \mid 8 \mid \text{O-16}}$, where all the $n = 1$ and $n = 2$ orbits are filled, and all others ($n = 3$, $n = 4$, etc.) are empty. Can there be a collision between two nucleons in $n = 2$ orbits? Our Condition (2) allows this collision only if both colliding particles end up in other $n = 2$ orbits, or if one goes into an $n = 3$ orbit and the other into an $n = 1$ orbit. But both alternatives are forbidden by our Condition (1) since all $n = 1$ and $n = 2$ orbits are already filled. Thus there can be no collision between nucleons in a closed shell nucleus—the neutrons and protons go around and around in the same orbits ad infinitum. They have no contact with their neighbors.

By similar reasoning it is easily shown that there can be no collision involving particles in filled shells of any nuclei in their normal state.* Thus, in a single

---

* In a normal nucleus all nucleons are in the lowest energy orbits available; the only unfilled shell is the one just above the highest full shell. Let us say the former is $n = 3$ and the latter is $n = 2$. According to condition (2), the only way there can be collision between an $n = 2$ and an $n = 3$ particle is if one of the particles ends up in another $n = 2$ or $n = 1$ orbit. But this result is contrary to condition (1) since all other $n = 1$ and $n = 2$ orbits are already full.

particle nucleus, such as $\boxed{8\;|\;9\;|\;\text{O-17}}$, the single neu-
tron in the $n = 3$ shell cannot have collisions with the
particles in the $n = 1$ and $n = 2$ shells. It may take pride
in being the fastest nucleon in the nucleus, but it lives
in total seclusion.

The simplest situation in which collisons can occur
is when there are two nucleons outside a closed shell,
as in $\boxed{8\;|\;10\;|\;\text{O-18}}$. A particularly interesting example
is shown in Fig. 2. Here we have two particles in

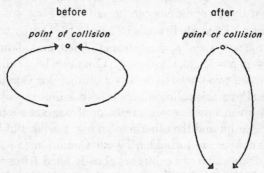

*Fig. 2.   This represents one type of collision that occurs
frequently in nuclei.*

the same orbit but moving in opposite directions; this
situation corresponds roughly in our scheme of quantum numbers to two orbits with the same n, l, and j
quantum numbers, but with the m quantum number
of one being the negative of the m quantum number
of the other. After the collision the two particles are
in a different orbit from the original one, but it is the
same orbit for both and they are moving in opposite
directions. Let us say, for example, that the (n, l, j, m)
quantum numbers respectively are:

Before Collision	*After Collision*
$\left\{\begin{array}{l}(3,\,2,\,\tfrac{5}{2},\,+\tfrac{5}{2})\\(3,\,2,\,\tfrac{5}{2},\,-\tfrac{5}{2})\end{array}\right\}$	$\left\{\begin{array}{l}(3,\,0,\,\tfrac{1}{2},\,+\tfrac{1}{2})\\(3,\,0,\,\tfrac{1}{2},\,-\tfrac{1}{2})\end{array}\right\}$

Let us see if our conditions for collision are satisfied. Condition (1) is satisfied by the fact that these orbits are all listed in Table II; since these are the only particles in $n = 3$ orbits, there is no problem of occupation of the orbits by other particles. The sum of the n values is 6 both before and after the collision, satisfying Condition (2). While we have not considered angular momentum in a quantitative way, it is perhaps intuitively obvious that the angular momenta of two particles moving in the same orbit but in opposite directions are equal in magnitude but opposite in direction: the total angular momentum is therefore zero. Since the value zero holds both before and after the collision, Condition (3) is satisfied. (We may also observe that the sum of the m quantum numbers is the same before and after the collision, being zero in both cases.) Condition (4) is satisfied because the sum of the l values is 4 before the collision and 0 after the collision, and both 4 and 0 are even numbers.

Thus we see that all the conditions are fulfilled; this type of collision can occur. As we may see in Table II, these pairs can obtain four other pairs of orbits by collision; namely,

$$\left\{\begin{matrix}(3,\ 2,\ 5\!/\!2,\ +3\!/\!2)\\(3,\ 2,\ 5\!/\!2,\ -3\!/\!2)\end{matrix}\right\},\ \left\{\begin{matrix}(3,\ 2,\ 5\!/\!2,\ +1\!/\!2)\\(3,\ 2,\ 5\!/\!2,\ -1\!/\!2)\end{matrix}\right\},\ \left\{\begin{matrix}(3,\ 2,\ 3\!/\!2,\ +3\!/\!2)\\(3,\ 2,\ 3\!/\!2,\ -3\!/\!2)\end{matrix}\right\},$$

$$\text{and}\ \left\{\begin{matrix}(3,\ 2,\ 3\!/\!2,\ +1\!/\!2)\\(3,\ 2,\ 3\!/\!2,\ -1\!/\!2)\end{matrix}\right\}.$$

The two neutrons in $\boxed{8\ |\ 10\ |\ \text{O-18}}$ continually undergo collisions that lead from one to another of these six sets of orbits. While our translation from quantum physics cannot be taken so literally that we should expect a collision every half turn around the orbit, it still is true that when there are two nucleons moving in opposite directions in the same orbit, collisions occur much more frequently than in any other situation.

From what has been said previously one might

think that the energy of a nucleus is exactly the sum of the energies of its occupied orbits. Actually this is not quite the true picture. It is the *average* interaction between a given nucleon and all the other nucleons in the nucleus that keeps it in orbit; thus, the orbit energies reflect only this *average* interaction. However, when two nucleons come close enough together to collide, there is an additional interaction not accounted for in that average. Collisions therefore affect the energy of a system.

In the particular example discussed for $\boxed{8 \mid 10 \mid \text{O-18}}$, a very interesting collision pattern can develop. The two neutrons pass from one to the other of the six pairs of orbits in a very regular and systematic way. We could say that their motion in this state is like a very rhythmic dance. As a result of these very frequent and regular collisions, the energy of the system is lowered to a considerable degree, so that this very rhythmic dance becomes the lowest energy state of that nucleus. It is therefore the state in which $\boxed{8 \mid 10 \mid \text{O-18}}$ is normally found.

The phenomenon that we have been describing is known as *pairing*. The energy lowering that it brings about is so great that the normal states of all nuclei have the maximum amount of pairing. That is, each nucleon not in a closed shell has a partner of its own type; each neutron has another neutron and each proton another proton with which it is paired. Each pair is at all times in the same orbit with its partner, but moving in opposite directions. They have very frequent collisions—some billions of trillions per second—which change their directions sending them into other orbits, but each is at all times in the same orbit as its partner moving in the opposite direction. The collisions do not occur randomly, but rather all the couples synchronize their collisions in such a way that the entire motion resembles a highly rhythmic dance. Actually these nucleons have a whole repertoire of dances, some more rhythmic than others. But in a normal nucleus they perform the most rhythmic dance in the repertoire.

Of course, the situation we have described is possible only if there is an even number of neutrons and protons. If there is an odd number of either—as, for example, in 29 | 34 | Cu-63 (the principal isotope of copper), which has an odd number of protons, 29—one particle must be without a partner. The odd particle very rapidly cuts in on one of the other couples, leaving one member of that pair without a partner; the latter very rapidly cuts in on another couple, and so on. There is at all times only one nucleon without a partner, but it stays without a partner for only about a billionth of a trillionth of a second before cutting in. Again, the collision pattern among all the nucleons in the unfilled shell—including the "cutting in"—is the most rhythmic one in the repertoire.

At this point you may have the impression that participation in this fantastic dance is limited to the nucleons in the unfilled shells, that the nucleons in the filled shells can only look on in envy as they go around endlessly in their same old orbits. In a large measure this is true, but very occasionally a pair of particles from the highest energy filled shells can defy the law of conservation of energy—item (2) in our list of conditions for collisions—and jump into the unfilled shell to participate in the dance. This situation does not last long, however, before a pair from the unfilled shell drops down into the lower shell to fill it once again. Because of the *uncertainty principle* (which will be explained in Chapter VI) the law of conservation of energy need not be obeyed strictly in quantum physics, but a defiance of this magnitude can endure for only a few ten-billionths of a trillionth of a second. For a pair of nucleons from filled shells of lower energy to jump up into the dance would require far greater defiance of the law. Such jumps happen still less frequently.

So far we have said nothing about collisions between neutrons and protons. In heavy nuclei (those with 50 nucleons or more) there are, as we shall see in Chapter IV, many more neutrons than protons; in the normal state the shell partially filled with protons already has its full complement of neutrons. In this situation, the rules stated at the beginning of this chapter do not allow collisions between neutrons and protons. Each neutron must be paired with another neutron, and each proton with another proton. There is a dance for protons and a dance for neutrons, with no intermingling between the two, although they do keep the same rhythm.

In smaller nuclei, especially those with fewer than 40 nucleons, the unfilled shells are the same for neutrons and protons, and our rules consequently do allow collisions between them. There is just one big dance for neutrons and protons (although there is still some preference for unmixed couples). Things get especially interesting in the few nuclei that have odd numbers of both neutrons and protons, as, for example, $\boxed{7\ |\ 7\ |\ \text{N-14}}$, the principal isotope of nitrogen. Here the odd neutron and odd proton do a very fancy dance which is much more complicated than the one pictured in Fig. 2—we will not even attempt to describe it here.

This, then, in admittedly rough translation, is our description of the structure of a normal nucleus. To recapitulate, the nucleons in the unfilled shell are paired off in couples doing a very rhythmic dance; if there is an odd nucleon, there is a continual pattern of cutting in. In heavy nuclei there are separate dances for neutrons and protons, but with the same rhythm, while in light nuclei there is just one grand mazurka for both. A pair of nucleons from the filled shell of highest energy occasionally jumps up into the dance, but must be replaced almost immediately by one of the couples from the unfilled shell. All the while the nucleons in the filled shells of lower energy circulate in their orbits in almost eternal boredom.

While the social life of a nucleon in a normal nucleus (at least for those nucleons in unfilled shells) is not an uninteresting one for those who like a rhythmic dance, the real action comes when a visitor arrives from the outside; that is, when the nucleus is struck by another nucleus which has happened to be passing its way. Such an event is known as a nuclear reaction, a subject we will discuss in Chapter VII. As an aftermath of a nuclear reaction, a nucleus is left usually in a state of higher energy than the normal one. These are known as *excited states,* in which the nucleons go into some of the other dances of their repertoire. Let us explore some of these.

Excited States—Other Dances in the Repertoire

Excited states have a higher energy than the normal state for any (or any combination) of the following reasons:

(1) The collision pattern may be less regular and coherent; that is, the dance may involve the same partners but be less rhythmic. It is surprising how large an energy difference this can cause.

(2) There may be one or more *broken pairs.* By a broken pair we mean that there are two nucleons (call them A and B) that move in orbits not shared by another nucleon moving in the opposite direction. These two will still have collisions with each other, and they may also have collisions with paired nucleons

(call them C and D) with the result that nucleon A becomes paired with nucleon C, while nucleons B and D remain unpaired. Many collisions of this general type occur, but after each collision there is still the same number of broken pairs. In our dance analogy, we may say that there are two or more nucleons without partners; they very soon cut in on other couples, leaving their partners free. These relinquished partners very soon cut in on other couples, and so on.

(3) Some of the nucleons may be excited to higher energy orbits, either in the same shell or in a higher energy shell.

(4) The shape of the nucleus may change from spherical to ellipsoidal, or if it is ellipsoidal in its normal state (as in the cases described toward the end of Chapter II), it may be spherical in some of its excited states.

(5) A nucleus of ellipsoidal shape can go into rotation much like the end-over-end rotation of a place-kicked football. (It is a strange consequence of quantum physics that a spherical system cannot rotate: when a perfect sphere rotates, it looks exactly the same as if it were not rotating, whereas there is no difficulty in determining whether a football is rotating end over end.)

Of course, there are many excited states with more than one of the features in the foregoing list. One can obtain catalogues listing vast numbers of states so complicated that we could never hope to set forth their structure here in any detail. However, some states are very simple and easily understood. Let us consider a few.

Perhaps the simplest excited states are those mentioned in Example (5) above, the rotational states of nuclei that in their normal states are nonspherical. These are their excited states of lowest energy. The nucleons do the same dance as in their normal state, but they swing slowly around as they go through it. It may be interesting to point out here that quantum physics requires that they swing around only at very specific rates. A typical rate would be one turn in the time an average pair of partners undergoes a dozen, or thereabouts, orbit-changing collisions. But there is a whole series of excited states in which they turn faster and faster. When they turn very fast, the dance pattern is affected somewhat, but not too greatly.

The lowest-energy excited states of most spherical nuclei are also very interesting; they are states in which the shape of the nucleus vibrates as shown in Fig. 3a. The motion is like the alternate compression and extension of a very flexible ball if one pushes inward and then pulls out at opposite points on the surface. The nucleus alternates between a pancake shape and a football shape. This vibration is a particular case of Example (2); it is a situation in which there is one broken pair but in which the collision pattern is very regular and coherent. At one instant the two unpaired nucleons have horizontal orbits, stretching the whole nucleus in the horizontal directions; then they undergo a collision that puts them both into vertical orbits, stretching the nucleus in the corresponding direction. The collision pattern takes the nucleons back and forth between horizontal and vertical orbits in a very regular rhythm—about 200 billion billion times a second. It is this regular rhythm that in most nuclei causes the energy of this state to be the lowest of any excited state. Its energy is considerably lower than that of states in which all partners are paired but in which the rhythm of the dance is not quite as perfect as in the normal state.

Other types of nuclear vibrations can occur from the development of special collision patterns, and these compose some of the most interesting dances in the repertoire. Two are illustrated in Figs. 3b and 3c. In Fig. 3b the nucleus resembles a pear in shape, or an egg, with the bulge (the stem end of a pear) going back and forth from one side to the other about a billion trillion times a second. In the dance pattern for this state one nucleon from a lower-energy filled shell jumps up into the dance, and so requires considerably more energy than the vibration shown in Fig. 3a. Both types of vibration are easily excited when a high energy nucleon in passing strikes a nucleus a glancing blow.

In the vibration shown in Fig. 3c, the neutrons and

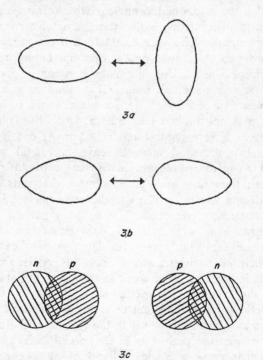

Fig. 3. Some of the interesting types of vibration are shown here.

protons behave somewhat as separate groups. When the neutrons go one way, the protons go the other. To excite this type of vibration requires a great deal of energy, but the state frequently occurs when a high energy gamma ray strikes a nucleus. A gamma ray, being an electromagnetic wave, is associated with a rapidly oscillating electric field, which shakes the protons back and forth but leaves the neutrons more or less undisturbed. It is not difficult to see how this sets up the vibration of Fig. 3c.

There are many other simple types of excited states. In a closed shell nucleus, as we have shown, there are no collisions and consequently no pairs to be broken; therefore vibrations of the type shown in Fig. 3a cannot occur. As a result, the excited state of lowest energy in $\boxed{8 \mid 8 \mid \text{O-16}}$ is one in which the shape of the nucleus is deformed into an ellipsoid. This is a simple case of Item 4 in the list. In another closed shell nucleus, $\boxed{82 \mid 126 \mid \text{Pb-208}}$, the lowest-energy excited state is the pear-shaped vibration shown in Fig. 3b.

In a single particle nucleus the lowest-energy excited states are those in which the single nucleon in an otherwise empty shell is excited to higher energy orbits in that shell. This description roughly holds for any nucleus with an odd number of nucleons; in the low-energy excited states all pairs remain unbroken, and only the odd nucleon is excited to higher orbits, but without affecting the dance pattern.

Because of their endless variety and great potential complexity, the study of the structure of excited states has long been, and still continues to be, a rich and fascinating field for investigation. It consumes a rather large fraction of the nuclear physicists' efforts.

CHAPTER IV

PARTICLE EMISSION PROCESSES AND NUCLEAR STABILITY

Let us see what happens when some of the nucleons in a nucleus are moving faster than is normal, as in one of the excited states described in the last chapter. Our first impulse is to think that they must "run out of gas" and slow down as would a car driven around and around a track. Cars require fuel to maintain their speed because motions in our everyday world are impeded by friction; a constant input of energy is needed to keep a constant velocity. But friction occurs only when materials rub against one another. There is no friction in atomic and nuclear motions, just as there is no friciton in the motion of celestial bodies. The Earth requires no input of energy to maintain its speed as it revolves around the Sun. Thus, there is no reason, in anything we have said, why the nucleons should not retain all their high energy just as the Earth does. However, they do not because there are certain processes in nature by which nuclei get rid of excess energy. The processes we are concerned with here are very peculiar ones; the excess energy acquired by a nucleus is given to a particle, which is then shot out of the nucleus at high speed! Since the nucleus loses energy in these events, they are referred to as *nuclear decay*. We can only be thankful that no such decay process is available for the Earth to reduce its energy. Even if we escaped being hit by the ejected particle or otherwise demolished in the catastrophe, the Earth, in losing energy, would move closer to the Sun, and we would all be burned up.

The next question one might ask is why these decay processes do not continue until the nucleons lose all their energy and come to rest. The answer is that the laws of quantum physics forbid it. The lowest energy they allow is the *normal state* described in the last chapter. This state ordinarily is reached very rapidly as a result of decay processes.

The particles emitted in these decay processes, veritable bullets shot out at speeds of tens of thousands of miles per second, have an important place in the history of nuclear physics. Scientists have developed methods of detecting them and measuring their properties, and it is from these measurements that much of our knowledge of what goes on in the nucleus has been derived.

There are three principal types of decay in nuclei: gamma-ray emission, beta decay, and nucleon emission. In this chapter we will describe them briefly and show how they limit the number of nuclei that are found in nature. These are generally nuclei which do not decay—such nuclei are called *stable*—or nuclei whose decay is so slow that it must be measured in billions of years or more. In the next chapter we will discuss in more detail what goes on in these processes.

Gamma-Ray Emission

Perhaps the simplest case of nuclear decay occurs when a nucleon is in a high energy orbit while a lower energy orbit is unfilled. In such a situation, the nucleon can jump to the lower energy orbit, while a bundle of electromagnetic radiation, known as a *photon,* is emitted. The photon carries off the energy given up by the jumping nucleon and represents the difference in energy between the original and final orbits. This process is exactly the same as the one in atoms where an electron drops from a higher to a lower energy orbit with the emission of a photon. In the case of the atom, energies of the photons are such that they stimulate the optic nerves of people; we call this radiation *light*. In the case of the nucleus the energies of the orbits, and therefore their energy differences, are very much greater than in atoms, and the energies of the photons consequently are very much higher. These photons from the nucleus are called *gamma rays*. Human evolution has not seen fit to provide us with sense organs for detecting them.

As a result of successive gamma-ray emission a nucleus in an excited state very rapidly decays to the lowest energy state possible for a nucleus with its particular number of protons and neutrons. Nuclei in excited states are therefore very rare in nature. When they do occur, they decay by gamma-ray emission in a minute fraction of a second.*

Beta Decay

Consider the nucleus of nitrogen-16 $\boxed{7 \mid 9 \mid \text{N-16}}$, which contains seven protons and nine neutrons. The occupied orbits are shown in Fig. 4. Note that since there are only eight orbits available in the $n = 1$ and $n = 2$ shells, one of the neutrons must be in the $n = 3$ shell, while one of the $n = 2$ proton orbits is not occupied. Now, think what would happen if a neutron could change into a proton. It could then have an $n = 2$ orbit, and consequently a much lower energy.

It turns out that there is a process in which a neutron *can* change into a proton, provided the energy of the system is lowered by its doing so. In this process, known as *beta decay*, two other particles, an elec-

---

* In a relatively few cases, the time for gamma-ray emission can be quite long. This situation will be discussed in the next chapter.

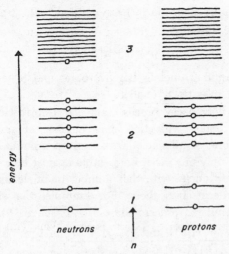

Fig. 4. The neutrons and protons in the nucleus of $\boxed{7\ |\ 9\ |\ \text{N-16}}$ *occupy these orbits.*

tron (e⁻) and an antineutrino ($\bar{\nu}$),* are emitted and the excess energy thus carried off. We can write the transition as

$$n \rightarrow p + e^- + \bar{\nu}.$$

The nucleus we have been discussing, $\boxed{7\ |\ 9\ |\ \text{N-16}}$, decays very rapidly by this transition, becoming a nucleus with 8 neutrons and 8 protons, $\boxed{8\ |\ 8\ |\ \text{O-16}}$.

Sometimes the energy of a system is lowered by a proton changing into a neutron. An example is the nucleus $\boxed{9\ |\ 7\ |\ \text{F-16}}$ in which the occupied orbits are as shown in Fig. 4 but with the labels "neutron" and "proton" interchanged. Here another beta decay process is available; a proton changes into a neutron while a positive electron (e⁺), otherwise known as a posi-

* An antineutrino is a very interesting particle which has no mass or charge. It always moves with the velocity of light—186,000 miles per second.

tron, and a neutrino (ν) are emitted.* The transition
may be written

$$p \to n + e^+ + \nu.$$

The resulting nucleus has 8 protons and 8 neutrons,
and again is $\boxed{8 \mid 8 \mid \text{O-16}}$.

The beta decay process causes transformations between nuclei with the same number of nucleons.
Therefore, of all nuclei with a given number of nucleons, only one or two are stable against beta decay.
All other nuclei with that number of nucleons eventually decay into them. For example, the electron
(e^-) emission process causes $\boxed{6 \mid 10 \mid \text{C-16}}$ to decay
into $\boxed{7 \mid 9 \mid \text{N-16}}$ and $\boxed{7 \mid 9 \mid \text{N-16}}$ in turn to decay
into $\boxed{8 \mid 8 \mid \text{O-16}}$. The positron emission process
causes $\boxed{10 \mid 6 \mid \text{Ne-16}}$ to decay into $\boxed{9 \mid 7 \mid \text{F-16}}$, and
$\boxed{9 \mid 7 \mid \text{F-16}}$ in turn to decay into $\boxed{8 \mid 8 \mid \text{O-16}}$. Thus
$\boxed{8 \mid 8 \mid \text{O-16}}$ is the only stable nucleus with 16 nu-
cleons.

One might conclude that stable nuclei have equal
numbers of neutrons and protons; and so it is for
lightweight nuclei. To cite a few random examples,
the only stable nuclei of atomic weights (i.e., nu-
cleon numbers) 12, 24, and 40 are $\boxed{6 \mid 6 \mid \text{C-12}}$,
$\boxed{12 \mid 12 \mid \text{Mg-24}}$, and $\boxed{20 \mid 20 \mid \text{Ca-40}}$ respectively,
all which have equal numbers of neutrons and
protons. But as the number of nucleons in the
nucleus increases, the electrical repulsion among
the protons becomes more and more important.
It causes the energies of protons to be higher
than the energies of neutrons in corresponding
orbits; consequently nuclei with more neutrons

* A neutrino is a particle very much like an antineutrino.

than protons become the stable ones. Thus the only stable nuclei of atomic weights 60, 118, 182, and 232 are $\boxed{28 \mid 32 \mid \text{Ni-60}}$, $\boxed{50 \mid 68 \mid \text{Sn-118}}$, $\boxed{74 \mid 108 \mid \text{W-182}}$, and $\boxed{92 \mid 146 \mid \text{U-238}}$ respectively. We see that in $\boxed{28 \mid 32 \mid \text{Ni-60}}$ there are 15 per cent more neutrons than protons, and this proportion increases to 36 per cent in $\boxed{50 \mid 68 \mid \text{Sn-118}}$, 46 per cent in $\boxed{74 \mid 108 \mid \text{W-182}}$, and 59 per cent in $\boxed{92 \mid 146 \mid \text{U-238}}$.

Nucleon Decay

In general, if a nucleus is highly excited, the excess energy will be distributed among many nucleons in a more or less random fashion. They collide with one another, frequently exchanging energy in the process until eventually by chance one nucleon happens to have an extra large share of the energy, and happens to be near the outside of the nucleus and headed in an outward direction. Just as the gravitational attraction of the earth cannot prevent a rocket from escaping if it is given a large enough outward velocity, so a nucleon with a large enough energy of motion directed outward will overcome the attractive nuclear forces of the other nucleons and come out of the nucleus. This process is "nucleon decay."

In addition to decay by emission of single nucleons, the same process allows groups of nucleons to come off if there is sufficient energy available. Of course, a group of nucleons is nothing but a nucleus in its own right, so we refer to this type of nucleon decay as nucleus emission. When large amounts of energy are available, as for example after a nucleus has been struck by a high energy particle, practically every known type of nucleus has been observed in emission. In most cases, emission of these nuclei requires even more energy than emission of a single nucleon, but there are some important exceptions.

Here we must discuss a rather technical term, the average *binding energy* (we call it B) of a nucleon in a nucleus. This B is the average amount of energy required to pull a neutron or a proton out of the nucleus if the whole nucleus were torn apart by pulling the nucleons out one by one. There are experimental methods available for determining B with very high precision. A plot of the results obtained for stable nuclei is shown in Fig. 5. Let us pause to discuss some of its aspects.

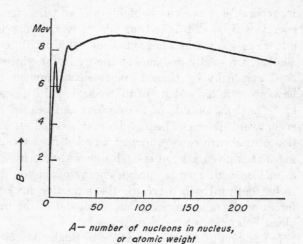

A— number of nucleons in nucleus, or atomic weight

Fig. 5. In this curve of binding energy per nucleon (B) versus atomic weight (A) the peak is at A = 4 and is $\boxed{2 \mid 2 \mid He\text{-}4}$.

First we note that B is less in light nuclei than in heavier nuclei. It is the attractive force of the other nucleons that holds a particular nucleon. If there are more nucleons, there is more attractive force; hence more energy would be required to pull the particular nucleon out. On the other hand, this increase in binding with increasing nucleon number does not continue very far; B levels out at about 8 MeV, mainly because the nuclear force falls off very rapidly at large distances. In a large nucleus most of the nucleons are too far away to exert very much attraction. (We mentioned in Chapter II that nucleons are kept at a respectable distance from one another by the repulsive nature of the nuclear force at very short distances, and by the Pauli exclusion principle.)

Another interesting feature of the curve in Fig. 5 is the falloff at large atomic weights. Mutual electrical repulsion among the protons, caused by the fact that they all have the same (+) electrical charge, is at work here. The electrical force does not fall off with increasing distance nearly as rapidly as does the nuclear force. Even in the largest nuclei the electrical repulsion between every pair of protons exerts an important influence.

There is one last important feature of the curve in Fig. 5 that bears mentioning; namely, the peak at $\boxed{2 \mid 2 \mid \text{He-4}}$. This is a closed shell nucleus with all neutrons and protons in $n = 1$ orbits. In nuclei with 5 nucleons the fifth nucleon must go into an $n = 2$ orbit. Since that orbit has a higher energy, less additional energy is needed to pull the fifth nucleon out of the nucleus. The binding energy therefore is lower. Thus, the curve goes down between atomic weights 4 and 5, giving the peak.

Since the binding energy of $\boxed{2 \mid 2 \mid \text{He-4}}$ is much greater than in other light nuclei, the situation is favorable for that nucleus, known as an *alpha particle*, to be emitted. For example, in a nucleus in a mass region where B is constant at 8 MeV, the binding energy of two neutrons and two protons is 4×8 MeV =

32 MeV in the nucleus, and 4×7 MeV* = 28 MeV in the alpha particle. Only 4 MeV ($32 - 28$) is required to release an alpha particle, as compared to the 8 MeV required to release a single nucleon. Such a nucleus when in an excited state of more than 4 MeV energy can decay by alpha-particle emission, whereas it must be excited by at least 8 MeV before it can emit a neutron or a proton.

For the heavier nuclei (that is, with larger nucleon numbers), the curve in Fig. 5 turns downward; less and less excitation energy is needed for emission of an alpha particle, until eventually none is needed. A very heavy nucleus even in its normal state can often decay by alpha-particle emission.† This process therefore limits the number of stable nuclei of high atomic weight. Herein lies the explanation of why elements heavier than uranium are not found occurring naturally on the earth.

Thinking back, we now can see in the drooping-down of the binding energy curve in Fig. 5 the explanation of the alpha-particle decay of heavy nuclei in the normal state. Remember that the electrical repulsion of the protons causes the downward curve. It is energetically favorable for two protons and two

* From Fig. 5, B is 7 MeV for | 2 | 2 | He-4 |.

† Recall that the curve in Fig. 5 is the *average* binding energy of all nucleons. For this to droop down, the binding energy of the last few nucleons must decrease much more. For example, for atomic weights 180 and 200, $B = 8.0$ MeV and 7.85 MeV respectively. Let $b =$ the average binding energy of the extra nucleons in the latter nucleus. Then $(180 \times 8.0) + (20 \times b) = (200 \times 7.85)$. Solving this gives $b = 6.5$ MeV. Since four of these would be bound by 7 MeV each in an alpha particle, alpha-particle emission would reduce the energy by $4 \times (7 - 6.5) = 2.0$ MeV. Thus alpha-particle emission is energetically favorable.

neutrons to be bound in an alpha particle rather than in a very heavy nucleus because in the latter the two protons are repelled by the large number of other protons. We might say that very heavy nuclei are sick from an overdose of protons, and they die from this illness by emitting an alpha particle. All elements on our Earth heavier than uranium already have died.

Another important type of nucleus decay is *fission,* the splitting of a nucleus into two nuclei of about the same mass. Consider, for example, as a possible decay process

$$\boxed{92 \mid 146 \mid \text{U-238}} \rightarrow \boxed{46 \mid 73 \mid \text{Pd-119}} + \boxed{46 \mid 73 \mid \text{Pd-119}}.$$
$$(1)$$

From Fig. 5 let us estimate the binding energy before and after this decay. For $\boxed{92 \mid 146 \mid \text{U-238}}$, $B = 7.6$ MeV per nucleon, whereas for the two $\boxed{46 \mid 73 \mid \text{Pd-119}}$ nuclei, $B = 8.4$ MeV per nucleon. The nucleons are bound by 0.8 MeV more energy after the decay than before. Since there are 238 nucleons involved, the total energy *released* in the decay process (1) is $0.8 \times 238 = 188$ MeV! Decay will lower the energy of the system greatly, and decay therefore can and does occur.

It should not be inferred from this example that fission always results in breakup into two equal mass fragments. Uusually it is more likely for the two fragments to be of rather different mass, as

$$\boxed{92 \mid 146 \mid \text{U-238}} \rightarrow \boxed{56 \mid 88 \mid \text{Ba-144}} + \boxed{36 \mid 58 \mid \text{Kr-94}}.$$
$$(2)$$

The question of the relative probability of the processes designated (1) and (2) depends on rather fine details of Fig. 5, among other things.

By similar reasoning we conclude that any nucleus for which the curve in Fig. 5 is lower than it is for nuclei of half the atomic weight can decay by fission. An examination of Fig. 5 reveals that this statement applies to all nuclei of atomic weight greater than about 100, including such familiar elements as silver, tin, iodine, tungsten, mercury, gold, and lead. All these can decay by fission, but fortunately, as we shall see, these decays occur at a very slow rate. The process does not limit the number of stable nuclei now existing on Earth. Even uranium, whose decay by fission is relatively rapid (that element would be mostly gone in 10 million billion years) decays 2 million times faster by alpha-particle emission.

Although naturally occurring fission is a very slow process, the addition of a little extra energy, as in a nuclear reaction, allows fission to occur at very great speed. It is this fact that makes possible many of the most important applications of nuclear energy.

CHAPTER V

HALF-LIVES

Characteristics of Decay Processes

When will a given nucleus decay? Quantum physics has an answer, simple and unequivocal, but the answer is somewhat startling. By quantum physics one can calculate the probability per second for a nucleus to decay; the average life of the nucleus before decay is the reciprocal of this probability. The half-life T is a more commonly used quantity simply related to the probability, being equal to 0.7 divided by the probability.

Though few people ordinarily think in such terms, the idea of probability of disintegration and of half-life is by no means uncommon, or even unfamiliar, in everyday living. The life of an electric light bulb, for example, can be so described. The manufacturer of the bulb issues a guarantee based on measurement of this probability. He runs a random sample of bulbs until they burn out, and sees how many burn out after

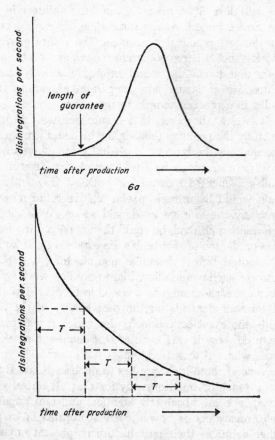

Fig. 6. Two rates of disintegration are shown here: (a) for light bulbs and (b) for nuclei undergoing decay.

various periods of time. The result of such a test would be as shown in Fig. 6a. Most burnouts would occur at about the same time, and not many would occur very much earlier or very much later. If the manufacturer sets the length of the guarantee period at the place on the curve shown, he can be confident that he will lose little money from bulb failures in the guarantee period. At the same time, he can advertise the longest practical guarantee. The utility of determining such a curve is therefore obvious, and we have seen that it can be found through the very simple procedure of seeing how long it takes various light bulbs in a random sample to burn out.

It is clear, however, that if someone were inclined to study the problem thoroughly, he could learn much more about the burnout probability for a given bulb. With a microscope he could search for flaws in the bulb's filament. He could find out how frequently the bulb would be turned on and off. He could measure precisely the voltage used, and so on. With all this information at hand, he could then make a fairly accurate prediction of that bulb's life expectancy. If he had a hundred bulbs of similar manufacture, a detailed study of each would allow him to predict which would burn out earlier and which would last longer. The time of burnout depends on the past history of the light bulb—the exact conditions under which it was manufactured, how it was handled, the temperature of the room where it was used, etc.

None of these ideas applies to nuclear decay! It is a basic tenet of quantum physics that all nuclei of a given type are absolutely identical and indistinguishable, regardless of how they were formed or of any other detail of their past history or present environment. It is therefore impossible *even in principle* to determine which nucleus will decay sooner and which later. All one can determine is the *probability* for decay, and this probability is the same whether the nucleus is at the center of the Sun or in the coldest and most empty regions of outer space. The probability of decay for a nucleus just formed in a nuclear reaction is no different from the probability for a nucleus that has been around for 10 billion years.

If we plot a curve of probability per second for disintegration of nuclei versus the time, we would therefore obtain a curve like that in Fig. 6b.

The number of nuclei decaying per second is the probability per second times the number of nuclei present. Since the latter quantity decreases as a result of the decays, the number decaying per second is largest at the beginning and decreases steadily thereafter. By the time half the nuclei have decayed—this is the half-life, T—the number decaying per second has dropped in half. Nuclei that have not decayed by this time still have the same probability per second of decaying, and so it takes another time interval equal to T for half of those to decay. By that time only a quarter of the original number remain, and consequently the number decaying per second is only one-quarter of the original rate. The process continues in this way; after each time interval T the number of remaining nuclei (and therefore the number decaying per second) drops in half. Moreover, the curve in Fig. 6b is the same whether or not all the nuclei were formed at the same time, and regardless of the environmental conditions. The difference between the curves in Fig. 6a and Fig. 6b is indeed striking; it results from the fact that a decaying nucleus is governed by the rules of quantum physics.

What Determines the Half-Life?

We may think of the half-life T as being determined by four factors: a characteristic half-life for the type of decay, τ; a term depending on the energy released in the decay, $f(E)$; the change of nuclear structure involved, S; and the difficulty encountered in penetrating barriers, P, about which we will have more to say. Combining these four factors, we obtain the following conceptual relationship, which we will call the *half-life formula*:

$$T = \frac{\tau \times S}{f(E) \times P}.$$

Each of the terms on the right side of this formula, τ, S, $f(E)$, and P, carries some very interesting information, so let us consider them separately.

The factor τ. The term τ (Greek letter tau) is a characteristic of the basic interaction that causes the decay. These interactions arise from the fundamental forces of nature; gamma-ray emission from the electromagnetic force, beta decay from the *Fermi interaction*, and nucleon emission from the nuclear force. These three, plus the gravitational force (which is far too weak to have any important consequences in nuclei), are the four fundamental forces known to science. Scientists have no way of predicting or explaining what forces exist in nature; they can only *discover* them, and observe how strong they are. No one has ventured to guess why these forces exist, or why they act as they do. They are just a part of this universe.

The discovery of new forces has been one of the great rewards of the study of the nucleus. For two and a half centuries all the phenomena known to exist in nature could be explained with reference to just two fundamental forces, the gravitational and electromagnetic. But within the first few years of man's study of the nucleus two new forces—the nuclear, and Fermi interactions—were discovered, investigated, and absorbed into the mainstream of scientific thought.

The determined values for τ for the various types of nuclear decay are:

$$\tau = 10^{-22} \text{ sec for nucleon emission*}$$
$$\tau = 10^{-15} \text{ sec for gamma emission}$$
$$\tau = 10^{-2} \text{ sec for beta decay}$$

These are defined so as to be about the shortest half-lives that can be expected for decay of nuclei by these modes. In the great majority of cases half-lives are longer than these values.

The values of τ are indices of the strength of the respective basic interactions; if the force were stronger, the probability for decay would be greater so that the half-life would be shorter. Thus, the Fermi interaction, which is responsible for beta decay, is relatively much weaker than the others; it is often referred to as the *weak interaction*. For equally obvious reasons, the interaction responsible for nucleon decay (this is the nuclear force that holds nuclei together) is sometimes called the *strong interaction*.

The factor f(E). The general rule for the factor $f(E)$ in the half-life formula is that it increases with increasing energy, E. The rate of this increase is somewhat different for the three types of decay, but in all three, if the energy released in the decay is larger, the probability per second for decay is greater and the half-life therefore shorter. We might see an analogy here to human motivation: if the reward for action is higher, the action takes place more quickly.

The factor S—*the effect of orbit changes.* The term

---

* For nucleon emission τ is the time required for a nucleon to reach the outside of the nucleus. We compute it by dividing the nuclear radius (about 10^{-12} cm) by the velocity of nucleons in the nucleus (about 10^{10} cm/sec) to get 10^{-22} sec. The strength of the nuclear force is the determining factor because the size of the nucleus and the velocity of nucleons inside depend on it.

S in the half-life formula is a measure of how much the motions of the nucleons must change in the decay. In gamma-ray emission a nucleon changes its orbit. If the new orbit differs only slightly in shape from the old one, and if the spin direction is the same for the two orbits, there is little impediment to the decay. Then S is a number close to unity. But if the orbit shape must change drastically, and if the spin of the nucleon must reverse, S can be as large as a billion or a trillion. We saw in Chapter II that the quantum number l governs orbit shape; for a more accurate description of this effect we must look to the change of this quantum number between the initial and final orbits.

Another important element in the determination of S is the fraction of the time the nucleon making the transition is in the prescribed orbits. Nucleons, as we saw in Chapter III, change orbits frequently as a result of collisions; this consideration could be very important. For example, if the transition takes a proton from orbit A to orbit B, and if orbit A is occupied by a proton in the original state only $\frac{1}{5}$ of the time and orbit B is occupied by a proton in the final state only $\frac{1}{3}$ of the time, S is increased by a factor of $3 \times 5 = 15$, and the half-life is lengthened by that factor.

In beta decay, where a neutron changes into a proton (or vice versa), S is determined by how much the neutron and proton orbits differ (as well as by the fraction of the time these orbits are occupied). If they are the same orbit (that is, if they have the same quantum numbers), S is just 1, but if the transition is between a circular and a very elliptical orbit (that is, the quantum number l changes drastically), S can be in the millions or billions. There is one interesting difference from gamma-ray emission here. In beta decay S is not dependent on whether or not the spins of the neutron and proton are in the same direction. A basic difference between the Fermi and electromagnetic interactions is involved here.

For discussion in any detail of nucleon emission we will wait until Chapter VII. It will be shown there that typically one orbital arrangement out of a thousand in a highly excited nucleus can result in nucleon emission. So S is about 1000. If less excitation energy is available, the fraction of arrangements leading to nucleon emission is much smaller. Hence, S can be a million or more.

In the emission of complex nuclei such as alpha particles or fission fragments, it would seem that a rather drastic rearrangement of orbits should be necessary, but in the framework of quantum physics these changes are not nearly so radical as one might imagine. Other things being equivalent, the S value for alpha decay or fission is usually only about ten times greater than for single-nucleon emission.

Complex Decays

The factor P in the half-life formula is important only when low energy protons or nuclei are emitted; discussion of it will be more appropriate in the next chapter. Putting together what we have learned of the other factors in the formula, we see that half-lives for nucleon emission are commonly in the range of 10^{-16} to 10^{-19} second, and half-lives for gamma-ray emission in the range of 10^{-14} to 10^{-8} second, except for a few rare cases where large changes in orbit shape are involved and the factor S is very large. In those cases half-lives can be as long as seconds, days, or years. These nuclei are known as *isomers*. Half-lives for beta decay are in the range of $\frac{1}{10}$ second to a few years, with exceptions of the kind noted for gamma-ray emission. The exceptions can make half-lives as long as billions of years.

This rather complete separation of half-lives for the three processes means that they very rarely compete with one another. Practically all nucleon emission is over in 10^{-14} second, before any appreciable gamma-ray emission can occur. Gamma emissions then occur and are essentially finished in much less than the $\frac{1}{10}$ second required for beta decay; by this time the nucleus is generally in its normal state. If the energy of the system can be lowered further by a proton changing into a neutron, or vice versa, beta decay then occurs.

Very often, the beta decay process leads to an excited state rather than to the normal state of the product nucleus. Then the excited state decays very rapidly by gamma-ray emission until the normal state is reached. Gamma-ray emission is such a rapid process that the beta and gamma emissions appear to occur simultaneously. In a very few cases beta decay leads to such a highly excited state of the product nucleus that nucleon emission is energetically possible. Nuclei of this type are known either as *delayed neutron emitters* or as *delayed proton emitters*. The former are very important in the control of nuclear reactors.

The fact that beta decay often has a half-life of days or years presents a unique opportunity; nuclei destined for beta decay can be chemically processed, shipped to various parts of the world, and used for industrial or medical applications, as will be discussed in Chapter VIII. Such nuclei are referred to as *radioactive isotopes—radioactive* meaning that they are *active* in emitting *radiation*. There are many radioactive isotopes that emit beta rays (and also gamma rays, as explained in the last paragraph). There also are radioactive sources that emit alpha particles and fission fragments. We will discuss them in the next chapter.

CHAPTER VI

BARRIERS AND THEIR PENETRATION

Among the most important concepts of quantum physics that must be taken into account if one is to get a picture of nuclear processes is the phenomenon of barrier penetration. Not only does barrier penetration control the rate of some types of decay through the factor P in the half-life formula; it also is the significant influence on the probabilities for many nuclear reactions, including all the thermonuclear reactions, whose great importance we will soon come to appreciate.

To understand this phenomenon, let us think of a cup of water on a table. Because of its height above the surface of the table (actually, because of its distance from the center of the Earth, but we'll ignore this complication), this water in the cup has a certain energy, and this energy would be lowered if the water flowed out of the cup onto the table. If the cup were to crack open, the water would in fact pour out over the table, which indicates that nature would favor this energy-lowering change. Nevertheless, while the cup remained intact the water would stay inside. A *barrier*, the side of the cup, would prevent the change. In order to get the water over the barrier, additional energy would be needed; the water would have to be raised over the rim of the cup.

Endless examples of barriers familiar to everyone could be cited. A *barrier* of dirt or stone or cement prevents a house from sliding down its hillside. *Barriers* prevent electric current from flowing through open switches, and coal (or, for that matter, all organic material, including people) from burning spontaneously in air. In each of these examples the action would lower the energy of the system, but there is not enough energy available to surmount the barrier.

While the integrity of barriers by and large seems formidable in our daily lives, this integrity is far from perfect in the world of quantum physics. The reason lies close to the heart of that subject, and is best explained to nonscientists in terms of the celebrated *uncertainty principles*. Only one of these will be used here. We may write it as

$$\Delta E \times \Delta t \cong 6 \times 10^{-22} \text{ MeV-seconds}$$

and we will refer to it hereafter as *the uncertainty principle equation*. It means that the energy of any particle (or group of particles) is subject to fluctuations, ΔE, for a length of time, Δt, given approximately by this equation. For example, energy fluctuations of 1 MeV can occur easily if they last no longer than 6×10^{-22} seconds. If they last five times longer, the left side of our equation is five times larger than the right, and the probability of occurrence is very much less. It can be shown that the probability is less by a factor of $10^{0.4 \times 5} = 10^2 = 100$. (The factor 0.4 in the exponent arises from a conversion from the base of natural logarithms to the base 10.)

It is not difficult to see that these short-term energy fluctuations can allow barriers to be surmounted. If the energy increases enough to bring the particle above the top of the barrier for a long enough time for it to traverse the width of the barrier, the particle can escape. In our water-in-the-cup analogy an energy fluctuation would be required that would raise the water to the top of the cup and give it an outward velocity for a time long enough for the water to get beyond the wall of the cup. If we test this process in our uncertainty principle equation, inserting the amount of energy and time required, the left side exceeds the right by a factor of about 10^{30}. In the terms of our earlier discussion, this statement implies that the event without our intervention would occur *once* in a time equal to $10^{0.4} \times 10^{30}$ multiplied by the length of time it would take for the water to flow out if the cup were cracked. This is a number containing 400 billion billion billion *digits!* Since the age of the universe in seconds is a number with only eighteen digits, we can be quite certain that the event will never occur. From this example we can see why penetration of barriers is not a part of our everyday experience.

When it comes to atoms or nuclei, however, the energy of barriers is much smaller. Twenty MeV, a typical barrier height in nuclei, is the energy required to raise a very tiny, barely visible droplet of water to a height equal to the thickness of a sheet of paper. Further, the width of barriers is much narrower (about 10^{-12} cm in nuclei), and the speed of motion much faster, so the time required for the particle to get past the barrier is much less (about 10^{-21} seconds). In some cases, therefore, barriers *can* be surmounted.

But first let us discuss the origin of barriers in nuclei. Consider an alpha particle that potentially might be emitted from a uranium nucleus. If it could escape far from the nucleus, the electrical repulsive forces between it and the remainder of the nucleus would be greatly reduced, and the energy of the system in consequence would be lowered. Alpha-particle decay is therefore energetically possible, and it turns out that 4.2 MeV of energy is released in the process. If the alpha particle travels only a short distance outside the nucleus, the electrical repulsive forces do not diminish very much—they vary rather slowly with distance. But such a move does require a great deal of energy to overcome the short-range nuclear forces between the alpha particle and the rest of the nucleus. Thus, a short move to just outside the nucleus requires a rather large *in*put of energy, amounting to about 20 MeV. Therefore, a *barrier* does block the alpha particle. While the energy of the system is lowered if the particle gets far away from the nucleus, an input of energy is required for it to get just a short distance outside. From similar reasoning, one can easily see that a barrier is encountered any time two electrically charged nuclear particles interact; but there is no such barrier for neutrons or gamma rays, which carry no electric charge.

If one inserts the quantitative numbers for the emission of an alpha particle from uranium, one finds that the left side of the uncertainty principle equation exceeds the right by a factor of only about 85, which is far less than the 10^{30} found in the case of the cup of water. In analogy with the illustration there, the alpha particle surmounts the barrier once in $10^{0.4 \times 85} = 10^{34}$ attempts. It must try 10 million billion billion billion times before it succeeds!

We can now use the formula to estimate the half-life for this alpha-particle decay. Taking $\tau = 10^{-22}$ sec, $f(E) = 1$, $S = 10^5$ (a very crude estimate from the discussions of the last chapter), and $P = 10^{-34}$ (from the last paragraph), we find

$$T = \frac{10^{-22} \text{ sec} \times 10^5}{1 \times 10^{-34}} = 10^{17} \text{ sec.}$$

Since there are 3×10^7 seconds in a year, the half-life by this computation is three billion (3×10^9) years; a more accurate value is 4.5 billion years.

Four and a half billion years is of the same order as the age of the Earth. It is not unreasonable, therefore, to conclude that a considerable fraction of the uranium present at the time of the formation of the Earth is still with us. If the half-life were much shorter—for example, if the barrier were penetrated once in 10^{32} attempts rather than once in 10^{34}—we would have no more uranium here on Earth. There could then be no atomic or hydrogen bombs. Indeed, we might never have discovered* that the nucleus exists!

The exponential character of the foregoing treatment suggests that the factor P is extremely sensitive to many details of the process. For example, the energy available for alpha decay in U^{238} (which we have been discussing) is 4.2 MeV and its half-life is 4.5×10^9 years, whereas in U^{237}, where the energy is 6.8 MeV, the half-life is 1.3 minutes. This tremendous difference is completely explainable by the energy difference in the calculation of P! The sensitivity of P to the energy available is truly tremendous.

For fission fragments, barrier penetration is very much more difficult. Consider a fission fragment in the same situation as the alpha particle of the previous example. The only difference is that the fragment's mass is about twenty-five times greater. For the same energy, the fragment's velocity is five times slower, whence the time required to get past the barrier, Δt in the uncertainty principle, is five times longer. Since Δt appears in the exponent, the barrier is penetrated only once in $10^{34 \times 5} = 10^{170}$ attempts. Fission fragments, you can see, are somewhat more like the "water-in-the-cup" than are alpha particles. Even for fission in U^{238}, where only about 6 MeV must be added to surmount the barrier, the half-life for spontaneous fission by barrier penetration is 10^{16} years. (Of course, if the nucleus is excited by 6 MeV, the energy is above the barrier and fission occurs in about 10^{-17} seconds.) It is then easy to see why fission occurs at an unobservably slow rate in all the elements from

* See *The Restless Atom* by Alfred Romer, Science Study Series S12, Doubleday & Company, Inc., 1960.

mass 100 to 230, even though it has been shown (in Chapter IV) to be energetically possible. Elements like silver, tin, iodine, tungsten, mercury, gold, and lead will stay around for a long, long time.

From the other end of the mass spectrum, barriers are very easily penetrated by positrons. The factor P is typically between 2 and 10 in that type of beta decay. For protons barriers are rather easily penetrated if they are not too high. However, proton emission with only a few MeV often is so slowed that gamma-ray emission occurs first.

Particles entering a nucleus, as well as those leaving it, encounter barriers, and the penetration problem is exactly the same. In laboratory experiments, reactions in which the incident particle has a very small probability for barrier penetration can never be observed. But, as we shall see in Chapters X and XI, very small penetration probabilities can be fantastically important for nuclear reactions in stars.

CHAPTER VII

NUCLEAR REACTIONS

Man's experience with chemical reactions goes far, far back into prehistory. Fire and the changes in food under heating, the fermentation of alcohol, the smelting of metals, the curing of animal skins—these are only a few of the chemical processes man for thousands of years has put to his own use. Chemical reactions, as we now know, occur when two or more atoms collide. In the collision the atoms may stick together to form a molecule; an electron may be transferred to form ions, or electron orbits may change and cause light to be emitted when they change back. It seems reasonable that analogous things should occur in collisions between nuclei. The fact is that they do occur, and we call these processes *nuclear* reactions.

But why should nuclear reactions be so unfamiliar in our daily life? Why were they not even discovered until the twentieth century? The answer is to be found if we think for a bit about the familiar electrical forces between charged particles. Because atoms are electrically neutral, there are no strong forces preventing two atoms from colliding. Nuclei, by contrast, carry large positive charges. They therefore repel each other very strongly until they get within about 10^{-12} cm of each other; then short-range nuclear forces become important. The strength of this repulsion is familiar as the force necessary to achieve a very large compression of a steel bar. In ordinary steel (as in any solid matter) the nuclei are about 10^{-8} cm apart. In order to bring the nuclei within 10^{-12} cm of each other, one would have to compress the length of the bar by a factor of 10,000. A steel girder the height of the Empire State Building would have to be compressed to a total length of 1 inch!

Still, a repulsive force does not always prevent a collision any more than an attractive force guarantees one. The planets do not collide with the Sun in spite of their strong gravitational attraction, but a prize fighter by blowing out his breath cannot prevent an approaching fist from colliding with his mouth. The other ingredient, clearly, is energy of motion, which depends on the mass and the velocity.* If two particles are on a collision course, their velocity of approach is slowed down by a repulsive force, but if

* Energy of motion, or *kinetic energy*, is $\frac{1}{2} mv^2$ where m is the mass and v is the velocity.

their initial energy is sufficiently large, they are not slowed to a stop and they *do* collide.

A simple calculation of the electrical repulsive forces shows that two iron nuclei would need a kinetic energy of 150 MeV in order to get within 10^{-12} cm of each other. Once they were within this distance, the short-range nuclear attractive forces would pull them together so strongly that nearly 150 MeV of energy would be released. The *net* energy needed for the two iron nuclei to have a reaction would be very small, the difference between 150 MeV and the slightly smaller energy released. The 150 MeV is the height of a barrier. However, we have seen that barriers are relatively impenetrable for heavy nuclei, and close to 150 MeV of kinetic energy actually is needed to make two iron nuclei react with any appreciable probability.

In ordinary matter, nuclei have some energy of thermal motion. It is well known that heat corresponds to a random motion of all the particles in a system, and that the average energy of each particle is proportional to the temperature. But even at the melting temperature of iron, this energy is only about 0.15 eV, or about a billion times too small for our hypothetical reaction. Thus, at the energies naturally available on earth, there can be no nuclear reactions. Nuclei must be accelerated artificially if they are to be made to collide. We will have more to say about accelerated nuclei later in this chapter.

Before going on to artificial accelerations, however, we must note two extremely important exceptions to what we have said. First, let us reconsider the arguments in terms of *hydrogen* nuclei.* The electrical

---

* In speaking of hydrogen nuclei we refer not only to the proton which is the nucleus of $\boxed{1\ |\ 0\ |\ \text{H-1}}$, but to *deuterons* and *tritons*, which are the nuclei of $\boxed{1\ |\ 1\ |\text{H-2}}$ and $\boxed{1\ |\ 2\ |\text{H-3}}$ respectively.

repulsion is proportional to the electric charge, and since a hydrogen nucleus has only $\frac{1}{26}$ as much charge as an iron nucleus (an iron nucleus contains twenty-six protons while a hydrogen nucleus contains only one), the energy required to bring two hydrogen nuclei to within 10^{-12} cm is $\frac{150 \text{ MeV}}{26 \times 26}$, or only about $\frac{1}{4}$ MeV. (Actually, the barrier is somewhat higher; hydrogen nuclei, being smaller, must come closer together than 10^{-12} cm before nuclear forces between them become strong.) Furthermore, since hydrogen nuclei are relatively lightweight, barrier penetration becomes an important factor. As a result, appreciable numbers of nuclear reactions can occur at energies as low as 10,000 eV (.01 MeV), or even 1000 eV. This energy is still thousands of times too low for ordinary earthly temperatures, but the temperature near the center of stars such as our Sun (or in hydrogen bombs) is high enough for such reactions to occur.* As we shall see, these reactions provide the energy which stars radiate and were largely responsible for the formation of the chemical elements, so nuclear reactions, though they do not occur naturally here on Earth, have been indispensable to the creation of Earth and to our lives on it.

The other exception concerns the reactions induced by one very special nucleus, the neutron, which carries no electric charge and is therefore not repelled by any nucleus it approaches. A neutron even at very low energy can produce nuclear reactions, and it is just such reactions that make atomic bombs and nuclear reactors work. However, very few free neutrons occur naturally on the earth, so even these nuclear reactions are not a part of our everyday experience.

* At a temperature of 10 million degrees, the average energy per particle is about 1000 eV.

Our treatment of the processes of nuclear reactions is long and must be somewhat detailed if a foundation is to be laid for understanding of some of the material in later chapters of this book. The reader whose interest in the nucleus is limited might skip here or there or, better still, go through the rest of this chapter hastily and return to it for review when reading the later chapters. To make the discussion as easy to grasp as possible, we resort to extensive subtitling to form a sort of outline.

Compound Nucleus Reactions

Consider a nucleus with the orbit energies shown in Fig. 7. In its normal state all $n = 1$, 2, and 3 orbits are filled, and a few nucleons are in $n = 4$ orbits. The $n = 5$ and $n = 6$ orbits are still below the escape energy, but they are completely empty. Suddenly, a fast-moving particle from the outside arrives on the scene. Let us say it is a 10 MeV neutron which, when it enters the nucleus, goes into an $n = 9$ orbit. There is a high probability for it to have collisions since the rules given in Chapter III restricting collisions are ineffective if there is sufficient energy for nucleons to be excited into the many unoccupied levels at high energy. For example, in a nearly head-on collision a nucleon in the $n = 2$ shell can receive enough energy to enter an $n = 6$ orbit, while the incident neutron is so reduced in energy that it enters an $n = 5$ orbit. Or, in a glancing collision a nucleon in an $n = 4$ orbit can be raised to an $n = 5$ orbit while the incident neutron ends up in an $n = 8$ orbit. (Note that the sum of the n values remains constant, as required by Condition (2) of Chapter III; $9 + 2 = 6 + 5$, and $9 + 4 = 8 + 5$ in our two examples.)

In the first example neither particle has enough energy to escape from the nucleus. In the second, the

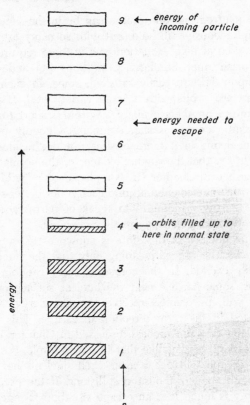

Fig. 7. For escape or nuclear emission to occur a nucleon must acquire the energy of the n = 7 orbit. When an incident particle enters the n = 9 orbit, a series of collisions occurs.

incident neutron can still escape, but there is an excellent chance that before it does it will have further collisions that reduce its energy to the region where it cannot escape; that is, to an orbit with $n = 6$ or less. Once all particles are in such orbits, further collisions occur with great rapidity. The requirements that each nucleon be in an allowed orbit and that no more than one neutron and one proton can be in the same orbit simultaneously still hold, but with so many orbits unoccupied at high excitation energy these requirements are easily met. Similarly, Conditions (3) and (4) of Chapter III are easily satisfied, since, in each shell, there are orbits with a large variety of l, j, and m quantum numbers available. Within a short time the available energy is shared among a goodly number of nucleons in a more or less random fashion. We might say that the rhythmic dance of the normal state, described in Chapter III, is replaced by a "wild orgy" in which nucleons bump into each other helter-skelter. It is hardly meaningful to speak of partners, so frequently and recklessly are they changed.

The nucleus in this state is known as a *compound nucleus,* the phrase meaning only that the nucleus is highly excited. In the course of these random collisions, some particle near the nuclear surface eventually will, by chance, receive enough energy and be headed in the right direction to escape. This is the nucleon emission process discussed in Chapter V. For excitation energies like that in our example, the average escape will occur after each nucleon has gone through about a thousand collisions. If the excitation energy is much less, an escape situation is much less probable since nearly all the energy must be concentrated on a single nucleon, and such a situation is very rare; a million or more collisions may occur before the proper situation for particle emission develops. The number of collisions is just the number of orbital configurations* the nucleus has gone through. If an average of a thousand collisions occurs before emission, we may conclude that only about one orbital configuration

---

* By an "orbital configuration" we mean essentially an arrangement in which some given sets of orbits are occupied by neutrons and protons, and all other orbits are unoccupied.

in a thousand leads to particle emission. This number is the factor S in the half-life equation. Thus, for very low excitation energies, S can be a million or more. These numbers have been used in Chapter V.

If the particle that happens to acquire the proper position and velocity for escape is electrically charged (as a proton or an alpha particle would be), it must, as it comes off, still face a barrier, as discussed in Chapter VI. Unless the energy is sufficiently high, there is a good chance that it will be turned back at the barrier, and the collision process starts all over again. Therefore, the emission of protons and alpha particles is generally less probable than neutron emission, especially in heavier nuclei where there are more protons giving larger electrical forces and consequently higher barriers. This probability is the factor P in the half-life equation.

Types of Compound Nucleus Reactions

It is conventional to designate a nuclear reaction by bracketing the incoming and outgoing particles, separated by a comma; for example, if the particle emitted in the reaction we have been discussing (recall that it was initiated by a neutron) is a neutron, a proton, or an alpha particle, we have an (n,n), an (n,p), or an (n,α) reaction respectively.

If the energy of the incident particle is sufficiently large, the nucleus remaining after emission of the first particle might have enough energy to emit another particle, say a neutron. We would then have an (n,pn), an $(n,2n)$, or an $(n,\alpha n)$ reaction for our three examples. If the energy of the incident particle is still larger, three or more particles can be emitted, so we might have $(n,3n)$, $(n,\alpha pn)$, $(n,2p3n)$, etc., reactions.

An important example of multiple particle emission occurs in the fission process. At fission the fragments break apart in a very distorted shape, as shown in Fig. 8. As the protrusion is pulled in, the nucleons in

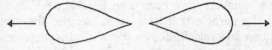

Fig. 8. Two fission fragments just after separation.

it are accelerated, and the energy they thereby accumulate is shared rapidly with the other nucleons. We thus have two ordinary, highly excited compound nuclei which, typically, decay by one or two neutron emissions. The fission process is therefore accompanied by the emission of a few neutrons, a very important fact for its application in energy production.

A compound nucleus, of course, can be formed in collision with particles other than neutrons. If the incident particle is a proton, we get (p,n), (p,p), (p,α), $(p,2n)$, etc., reactions; if it is an alpha particle we get (α,n), (α,p), etc., reactions; similarly, if the incident particle is an H^2 nucleus (deuteron), an iron nucleus, or any other conglomeration of nucleons.

A compound nucleus can be formed also when a gamma ray or an electron strikes a nucleus. They act only through the electromagnetic interactions (with the protons), and generally are much less effective than nucleons in exciting a nucleus. If their energy is less than about 8 MeV, the compound nucleus formed does not have enough energy for nucleon emission;* it can decay only by gamma-ray emission back to the original nucleus. Since gamma-ray emission is very rapid, low energy gamma rays and electrons cannot make radioactive nuclei with long half-lives.

* Recall from Fig. 7 that the energy required to remove a nucleon from a nucleus is about 8 MeV.

Cross Sections

The probability that an incoming particle will induce a nuclear reaction is determined by what is technically called the *cross section* for that reaction. It may be thought of as the target area presented by the nucleus to an incident particle; if the latter strikes within this target area, the reaction will occur. Typical total cross sections for 10 MeV neutrons to induce nuclear reactions are about 10^{-24} cm^2.

The probability per centimeter of travel for an incident particle to induce a reaction is equal to the cross section times the number of target nuclei per cubic centimeter in the target material. Any veteran of a high school chemistry course can easily calculate that for a solid material the latter quantity typically is about 10^{23}, whence by multiplying this by 10^{-24} we find that the reaction probability is about $\frac{1}{10}$ per centimeter. This means that on the average a neutron will induce a reaction after going about 10 centimeters (four inches).

Low Energy Reactions

The picture we have outlined is valid only if the particle initiating the reaction has several MeV of energy. A very interesting and important variation occurs if the incident particle has an energy much less than 1 MeV. An electrically charged particle with such a low energy is so strongly repelled that it rarely is able to enter the nucleus. But if the incoming particle is a neutron its probability for entering a nucleus actually increases rapidly as its energy is lowered—the basic reason for this is that it spends more time near the nucleus as it passes. In some cases cross sections become as large as 10^{-20} cm^2, ten thousand times the typical cross section we have given for high energy neutrons. These large reaction probabilities lead to some interesting applications, so let us study this situation in more detail.

Consider a slow-moving neutron approaching, say, a ⊡ 26 ⊡ 30 ⊡ Fe-56 ⊡ nucleus. If the neutron strikes, a nucleus of ⊡ 26 ⊡ 31 ⊡ Fe-57 ⊡ will be formed, and it will have an excitation energy equal to the energy of the neutron plus its binding energy, which we found (in Fig. 7) to be about 8 MeV. In this region of excitation energy a nucleus has a great many excited states, but they are still well separated from each other. As a consequence, a neutron cannot enter a ⊡ 26 ⊡ 30 ⊡ Fe-56 ⊡ nucleus unless its energy is right for forming one of these states.* A plot of the cross section of ⊡ 26 ⊡ 30 ⊡ Fe-56 ⊡ for neutrons of various energies therefore looks somewhat like Fig. 9. It is characterized by *resonances*, peaks in the cross section occurring where the energy is just right to form an excited state of ⊡ 26 ⊡ 31 ⊡ Fe-57 ⊡. It is relevant to point

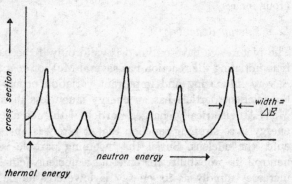

Fig. 9. *Cross section of neutrons of various energies which form a compound nucleus.*

* The fact that nuclei can exist only in certain states having very particular energies is a very general consequence of quantum physics.

out here why these resonances are not infinitely sharp; they have a finite width, ΔE, given by the uncertainty principle. In this case, Δt is the half-life, T, for decay of the state of $\boxed{26\,|\,31\,|\,\text{Fe-57}}$ that is formed. The point here is that the neutron must have the correct energy to reach a state of $\boxed{26\,|\,31\,|\,\text{Fe-57}}$ because conservation of energy requires it. However, if the state only lasts for a time T, energy need not be conserved more accurately than given by the uncertainty principle with $\Delta t = T$.

At higher energies (such as those discussed in the last section) the half-lives of the states become much shorter. The resonances therefore widen until they are wider than the distance between resonances, and then the cross section varies smoothly with energy.

In some circumstances a free neutron can have enough collisions with surrounding nuclei to bring it into thermal equilibrium; that is, its average kinetic energy is the same as the average kinetic energies of the atoms in its vicinity. At room temperature this energy is about 0.025 eV, which comes very low on the scale of Fig. 9. From that figure it is apparent that the cross section for thermal neutrons depends very much on how close a resonance happens to be to thermal (effectively zero) neutron energy. This is more or less a matter of chance, depending on the exact location of nuclear states at about 8 MeV excitation energy. Consequently, variations in *thermal-neutron* cross sections are very large. For example, the average distance traveled before a nuclear reaction is induced is about 0.0003 inches in Cd^{113},* which hap-

---

* Cd^{113} is a short notation for $\boxed{48\,|\,65\,|\,\text{Cd-113}}$. It will be used henceforth in cases where the number of protons and neutrons are not of particular importance. These numbers can readily be deduced from the atomic number and atomic weight by reference to the Appendix.

pens to have a strong resonance very near to thermal energy. The corresponding distance is 0.01 inch in U^{235}, 2 inches in U^{238}, and a quarter mile in Pb^{208}!

Once a slow neutron enters, the excited (compound) nucleus that is formed has barely enough energy to emit a neutron; correspondingly, in accordance with our previous discussion, the factor S becomes very large. If the energy is low enough—say, below 100 eV—S exceeds 10^8; according to our half-life formula the half-life for neutron emission is therefore longer than 10^{-14} seconds. According to our half-life formula and the values of τ given in Chapter V, the nucleus can decay by gamma-ray emission in about 10^{-14} seconds. This process may therefore occur before neutron emission if the incident neutron energy is less than about 100 eV. If the incident neutron energy is much lower (as in thermal neutrons), gamma-ray emission predominates.* Once a gamma ray has been emitted, there is no longer sufficient energy for neutron emission. The nucleus decays to its normal state in a series of further gamma-ray emissions. The net result is that a neutron is captured, and no nucleon is emitted. This process is referred to as an (n,γ), or *neutron capture* reaction.

While neutron capture is generally the most probable process when thermal or very low energy neutrons induce nuclear reactions, there are a few extremely important exceptional cases where the entrance of a slow neutron supplies enough excitation from its binding energy to allow *nucleus emission*. For example, in uranium, we said, the additional energy required to produce fission is only a few MeV. In U^{235} (but not in U^{238}) the binding energy of a captured neutron is sufficient to supply the requirement, at which

---

* For very low neutron energies, the factor $f(E)$ in the half-life formula is also important in inhibiting neutron emission.

point thermal neutron irradiation of U^{235} usually leads to fission. This is the vital reaction for nuclear energy production on the Earth. If the barrier were only 1 per cent lower so that thermal neutrons could produce fission in the much more abundant isotope U^{238}, atomic bombs would have been much easier to make, and Germany would very probably have been the first nation to make them—in 1939. Fortunately, thermal neutrons on U^{238} give only (n,γ) reactions.

Another of the few exceptions where thermal neutrons do not lead to simple neutron capture is in $\boxed{3\,|\,3\,|\,\text{Li-6}}$, where the compound nucleus, $\boxed{3\,|\,4\,|\,\text{Li-7}}$, decays into $\boxed{1\,|\,2\,|\,\text{H-3}}$ + $\boxed{2\,|\,2\,|\,\text{He-4}}$. This is the principal process for production of tritium $\boxed{1\,|\,2\,|\,\text{H-3}}$, which is the fuel for hydrogen bombs and may someday be the fuel for thermonuclear power.

We have said that low-energy charged particles like protons have difficulty entering a nucleus because of the electrical repulsion. They can do so only in relatively light nuclei, and there only by barrier penetration so the cross section is very small. Once they have been captured, the compound nucleus formed often has sufficient energy to decay in only one of two ways, by proton emission or gamma emission. At low energies the barrier penetration probability is so small that the half-life for proton emission is much longer than 10^{-14} seconds; gamma-ray emission therefore occurs first and we have a (p,γ) reaction. By completely analogous reasoning, (α,γ) reactions can also occur at low energy. These reactions are characterized by resonances just as in the case of neutrons, but their cross section decreases very rapidly with decreasing energy, due to the decreased probability for barrier penetration.

Direct Reactions

The compound nucleus type of nuclear reaction that
we have been describing occurs most frequently and
is of enormous practical importance, but the nuclei it
produces are of so complicated a structure that they
probably will never be understood in detail. Fortunately, however, there are other types of nuclear reactions which disturb the orbital system described in
Chapters II and III in a very simple way. These reactions therefore have been enormously useful in
helping us to understand it. They are classed under
the general category of *direct reactions*.

Perhaps the most interesting of the direct reactions
is known as *stripping*. A deuteron (the nucleus of
$\boxed{1 \mid 1 \mid \text{H-2}}$), which consists of a neutron and a proton, is shot at a nucleus; the neutron enters the nu-
cleus, while the proton is deflected from the incident
direction but continues on its way and can be detected by an experimenter. Thus we have a (d,p)
reaction, which is essentially a fancy way of inserting
a neutron into a nucleus. When the neutron is inserted
it must go into one of the allowed orbits of Chapter
II. But from conservation of energy the experimenter
knows that the energy of the proton he has detected
depends on the energy of the neutron. Since the neutron's energy is the energy of the orbit it entered, the
experimenter thus has a means of studying the allowed orbits and their energy. Of course, if the orbit is already filled, a neutron cannot be inserted.
Thus, by noting the ease with which neutrons can be
inserted into various orbits the experimenter can determine to what extent they are occupied.

Similar information can be obtained from the in-
verse reaction, (p,d), known as *pickup*. When a proton is shot in, it picks up a neutron from the nucleus,

and the two come off as a deuteron, which can be detected experimentally. This reaction gives information on the orbit the neutron was in before it was picked up, and on the extent to which that orbit was occupied.

Another type of direct reaction is *inelastic scattering*. The incident particle strikes the nucleus a glancing blow, setting it into vibration or rotation, and comes off with reduced energy. The amount by which its energy is reduced, an easily measurable quantity, gives the energy involved in the vibration or rotation. Other measurements such as the angle of deflection and the cross section give the type of vibration and its amplitude.

From the Practical Viewpoint

Up to this point we have been discussing the microscopic details of nuclear reactions. Before leaving the subject, we should look at the matter from a large-scale, more practical point of view. A beam of particles, let us say protons from an accelerator, is directed at a target—a piece of copper, for example. If the proton energy is high enough, many nuclear reactions occur, including (p,n), (p,p) (p,α), $(p,2n)$. Energetic particles come off in all directions. Among them are neutrons—such nuclear reactions providing the only means we have of making neutrons. At the same time (actually after about 10^{-14} to 10^{-9} second) gamma rays are emitted as the residual nuclei *de-excite* to their normal states, and so we have also a copious source of gamma rays. In most nuclear reactions the final nucleus is not the same as the original one and is very likely to be unstable against beta decay. For example, the (p,n) reaction on $\boxed{29\,|\,36\,|\,\text{Cu-65}}$ leads to $\boxed{30\,|\,35\,|\,\text{Zn-65}}$, the nucleus with one more proton and one less neutron, and this nucleus beta-decays with a half-life of 250 days back to Cu^{65}. Such a long half-life makes Zn^{65} suitable for use in medical and engineering research, as will be discussed in Chapter VIII. Nuclear reactions are the only means of producing radioactive isotopes. Gamma-ray emission follows the beta decay, so we have a radioactive source of both beta and gamma rays.

During the bombardment, we also could have made measurements on the particles emitted from the nuclear reactions or on the gamma rays (or both) in order to study nuclear structure problems, or to study the mechanisms of nuclear reactions. We could use the radioactive isotopes produced to study nuclear structure problems, or perhaps to study basic problems in the beta decay process.

If the reactions occur in a reactor (or a bomb), it is a simple matter to absorb with surrounding matter the energy of the particles emitted in the reactions, and in the beta and gamma decays which follow them. The energy is thereby turned into heat, which can be changed into other useful (or destructive) forms of energy.

Nuclear reactions have an important place in all applications of nuclear physics, and have figured in much of the scientific work that has led to our understanding of the nucleus. In Chapters X and XI we shall discuss how nuclear reactions provide the energy which the Sun (like other stars) radiates, and how they were responsible for the formation of the chemical elements of which all matter is composed.

CHAPTER VIII

RADIATION

The beta rays, gamma rays, nucleons, and nuclei (like alpha particles) that come off when nuclei, in the proper circumstances, decay are generally grouped together in public discussion and spoken of as *nuclear radiations*. It is common knowledge that they can be extremely dangerous. On the other hand, scientists have done a great deal of useful work with them, from improving auto engines to treating cancer. In this chapter we will look at the science behind some of these applications.

When a rapidly moving electrically charged particle (such as an electron or a proton) passes through a material substance, it exerts an electrical force on the electrons in the substance, knocking them out of their atoms. The energy required to do this comes from the energy of motion of the fast particle, so that its speed is slightly diminished; after a million or so of these interactions, it is stopped. The thickness of material required to stop the particle is greater for particles of lighter mass and higher energy. It varies from 0.25 inch for an electron of relatively high energy to less than 0.001 inch for fission fragments and the alpha particles encountered in radioactive decays. If one knows the type of particle, one can calculate the amount of energy it will lose in traversing a given thickness of a given material. This process is the basis for thickness gauges now used in industry. For example, by interposing a foil between an alpha-particle source and a suitable detector, and measuring the amount by which the alpha-particle energy is decreased, one can easily determine the thickness of the foil to 0.00001 inch.

Another type of thickness gauge uses beta rays instead of alpha particles. Beta rays are emitted with a wide range of energies—the total energy released is shared in various proportions between the electron and the neutrino—and the thickness of absorbing material between the source and detector consequently determines the number of electrons that are stopped. The thickness can be determined simply by counting the number of electrons reaching the detector, a much easier job than measuring energies.

The fact that electrons, protons, and other charged particles knock electrons off the atoms to which they are attached has several important implications. First, these electrons are responsible for the forces which bind atoms together to make molecules; their removal often destroys or changes the molecule. This is the basis for the biological effects of radiation. If enough molecules in a cell are destroyed, the cell will die, and if enough of its cells are dead, an organ will cease to function. This effect is especially severe in rapidly multiplying cells. Since cancerous cells multiply much more rapidly than normal ones, they are preferentially destroyed, but it is still a tricky business to administer enough radiation to kill all the cancerous cells without destroying too many normal cells in the vicinity. Another example of rapidly multiplying cells being destroyed preferentially is in the early stages of development of the human fetus. Many sad effects have been noted in children whose mothers were exposed in pregnancy to the Hiroshima bombing.

Molecules that carry genetic information are extremely complex, and even slight changes in their structure can cause important mutations, changes in the inherited physical characteristics of the offspring.

Moreover, succeeding generations inherit these changed characteristics, and the changes accumulate if the successive generations are exposed further to radiation. Enough of these changes, no matter how slowly accumulated, could radically alter or destroy the human race.

A second consequence of the fact that energetic charged particles knock large numbers of electrons off the atoms to which they are attached is that these electrons can be collected easily when an electric voltage is applied. The process of collection gives an electrical pulse whose size is proportional to the number of knocked-off electrons, and this number in turn is proportional to the energy of the original particle. Since electrical pulses can be readily measured with standard electronics techniques, one can easily detect the passage of a single electron or proton, and determine its energy. The devices used are known as *counters;* they count individual particles. Various types of counters have been developed—Geiger counters, scintillation counters, semiconductor counters, etc. The first two of these have attained a distinction rarely awarded to scientific apparatus—they are listed in the Sears-Roebuck catalogue.

Since counters can detect the decay of a single nucleus, they give an extraordinarily sensitive measurement of amounts of material. A few thousand atoms decaying with a half-life of one hour are detected easily—they give about one count per second. On the other hand, the smallest number of atoms that can be detected by conventional means is about a million billion, the number of atoms weighing a billionth of an ounce. The use of counters on radioactive atoms is thus a trillion times more sensitive.

This sensitivity makes possible many important applications. For example, one can study the lubricating efficiencies of various oils in automobile engines by incorporating radioactive material in the piston rings. When the rings wear, the radioactive material gets into the lubricating oil, where counters detect it. More efficient lubricating oils reduce the wear, and thus the amount of radioactivity in the oil.

There are medical as well as engineering applications of this sensitivity. Arsenic in the human body collects preferentially in brain tumors. By feeding a patient a very small amount of radioactive arsenic isotope ($\boxed{33 \mid 41 \mid \text{As-74}}$), the diagnostician can determine very accurately the location of a brain tumor because the arsenic collects there and can be detected by the gamma rays it emits. Retention of water in the body can be measured by closely related techniques. The subject drinks a glass of water in which some of the ordinary hydrogen is replaced by the radioactive hydrogen isotope $\boxed{1 \mid 2 \mid \text{H-3}}$ (tritium). The beta rays emitted from this isotope in urine samples at various later times give an accurate measure of the length of time the water remained in the body.

This last application is an example of the much-used *tracer* technique. A particular chemical element is *tagged* by mixing in a small amount of one of its radioactive isotopes. Because isotopes are chemically identical to the stable atoms of the element, the mixing is thorough. By detecting the emitted radiations it is then easy to follow the element through various chemical and biological processes. Some of these processes may involve reactions with the same element from another source, but there is no confusion between atoms from the two sources because those from the first are tagged while those from the second are not.

Because neutrons and gamma rays are not electrically charged particles, their interactions with matter are not explained by the second paragraph of this chapter. Gamma rays interact principally by cata-strophic collisions with electrons in which most of the energy, if not all, is transferred to the electron. The resulting high energy electron is an electrically charged particle which acts as described above. Neu-trons interact only by nuclear collision, and in each interaction at least some fraction of their energy is transferred to charged particles, the struck nucleus or the products in reactions such as (n,p) or (n,α). If the neutron just bounces off the struck nucleus—this is called an *elastic* collision—or if the reaction products are neutrons, the emitted neutrons will undergo further collisions with other nuclei until even-tually all the energy is transferred to charged particles or gamma rays.

Thus, neutrons or gamma rays produce the same sort of effects as charged particles, but there is one very important difference: charged particles are stopped in a small fraction of an inch, whereas neu-trons or gamma rays typically go several inches be-fore interacting at all and a small fraction even go through several feet of material. Consequently, alpha or beta particles can damage only the skin, but gamma rays can penetrate to the reproductive organs to cause genetic damage or other internal destruction. (Of course, this limitation on damage from alpha and beta particles does not apply if radioactive materials enter the body through the respiratory or digestive systems.)

The ability of gamma rays to penetrate can be ap-plied to useful ends. Radiation can preserve some food from spoilage by killing the microscopic organ-isms that cause decay. Electrically charged particles (protons or electrons) cannot be used since they would stop near the surface and not penetrate the food. Neutrons are not usable—they would make the food radioactive. Low energy gamma rays, however, do penetrate and, as we have seen in Chapter VII, do not cause radioactivity. They have been widely used for this purpose.

Gamma rays are used also to determine how full a container, such as a grain storage bin, may be. In one method, a source and a detector are mounted on opposite sides of the bin, and moved up and down together. When they get above the level of the grain, the gamma rays are no longer stopped, and the count rate increases. Here again the penetrating power of gamma rays is necessary. Other particles would be stopped in the bin walls, or by the air in the bin.

Neutrons, as we have seen, are produced only in nuclear reactions and are neither dangerous nor useful except in the vicinity of accelerators or reactors (or bombs). However, there are some useful applications of the great ability of neutrons to penetrate. For example, there has been some success in treating cancer by implanting boron in the affected area and irradiating the patient with low energy neutrons. Since the reaction $\boxed{5 \mid 5 \mid \text{B-10}}$ (n,α) $\boxed{3 \mid 4 \mid \text{Li-7}}$ has a very large cross section, alpha particles are released in the cancerous material. The distance they travel is so small that no damage is done to the rest of the body.

Another interesting application of neutrons is in *activation analysis,* to determine the amount of some element in a substance by inducing a nuclear reaction and detecting the resulting radioactivity. For example, suppose we want to know the amount of copper in an object. We insert the metal into a nuclear reactor where it is irradiated with neutrons. Some of the copper atoms undergo the reaction Cu^{63} (n,γ) Cu^{64}; the product Cu^{64} decays by beta and gamma emission with a half-life of 13 hours. After a while, the object is removed, copper is chemically separated (although the amount present may be invisible), and the intensity of activity with a 13-hour half-life is measured with a counter. The amount of copper can be determined rather accurately even if it is present in a concentration of less than one part per million.

One of the most interesting applications of nuclear radiations is in the determination of the ages of materials. Since uranium transforms into lead by a series of alpha and beta decays with a known half-life, one can determine the age of a rock by the ratio of uranium to lead contained in it.* For example, if we found equal amounts of lead and uranium in the rock, we would know that half the uranium had decayed since the rock was formed, and hence we would conclude that the age of the rock was just the half-life of uranium, or 4.5 billion years.

The nucleus C^{14} (carbon-14) is produced in the nitrogen of the atmosphere by cosmic-ray neutrons in the reaction $\boxed{7\,|\,7\,|\,\text{N-14}}$ (n,p) $\boxed{6\,|\,8\,|\,\text{C-14}}$; it undergoes beta decay with a half-life of 5600 years. The C^{14} mixes with the other carbon atoms in the atmosphere (principally in carbon dioxide) since they are chemically identical, and this mixture is taken up by growing things. Thus in a tree a certain fraction of the carbon atoms are C^{14}. But if the tree is chopped down and some object made of the wood, the C^{14} will decay, and after a few thousand years the fraction of all carbon that is C^{14} will have decreased. The amount of C^{14} per unit weight of carbon—this measurement is obtained easily by counting the beta rays emitted—therefore gives the age of a wooden object. The Dead Sea Scrolls, for only one of many examples, have been dated to A.D. 40 by this method.

There are many other techniques for dating objects

---

* The lead produced by the decay of natural uranium is Pb^{206}, which is easily distinguished from normal lead which is mostly Pb^{208}.

by measuring the natural radioactivities, and the periods of time to which they can be applied range from a few years to billions. The results have been indispensable in arriving at pictures of the past that have been put together through geology, archaeology, and other fields of research.

This discussion of the applications of nuclear radiations is far from complete, and was not meant to be otherwise. Nor does it pretend to offer a uniform coverage. The only purpose was to give an impression—no more—of the methods and their uses in science, medicine, and industry, and of their great potential for further applications.

CHAPTER IX

NUCLEAR ENERGY—ON EARTH

Nothing is more vital to modern society than sources of energy to do man's work. The enormous use of electrically powered household appliances, so familiar to us all, is only a minor example. Industry and agriculture depend almost altogether nowadays on powered machinery, and nearly every new technological advance brings demand for more energy. Up until now the world has got nearly all its energy from water power and from coal, oil, and other fuels burning in chemical reactions, but the supply of these combustible materials and of water for power is very limited. Competent studies have concluded that the known deposits of coal and petroleum will be sufficient for only a hundred years or so. If our society is to continue to flourish, other sources of energy must be tapped, and the only potentially available sources are of nuclear origin. The principal processes producing nuclear energy are *fission* and *fusion,* which are the subject matter of this chapter.

Power from Fission

The fission reaction we already have discussed in several contexts. We found that it is the splitting of a heavy nucleus into two roughly equal parts. These fragments come off with a kinetic energy of about 170 MeV. This energy is lost rapidly in the process of knocking electrons off atoms (as discussed in the last chapter). The energy received by the electrons is dissipated in collisions and appears as heat energy. Further energy is released in the form of beta and gamma rays after the fission fragments are stopped. The heat energy produced amounts to a total of about 190 MeV per fission.

It may be of some interest to compare the energy release from this nuclear reaction with the energy release from the chemical reactions in the burning of chemical fuels such as coal, oil, etc. Since chemical reaction energies are of the order of electron-volts (eV) while nuclear reaction energies are of the order of millions of electron volts (MeV), we might expect the yields of the latter to be about a million times higher. To be more specific, if one multiplies the 190 MeV of energy released per fission by the number of U^{235} atoms in a pound, and applies a factor for converting from MeV to the more practical energy unit, Calories, one finds that "burning" of U^{235} by fission gives an energy release of 8 billion Calories per pound. From the burning of more conventional fuels the following energies are obtained:*

* Some of these numbers are familiar to dieters as the Calorie content of butter or fats (the same as oil), or of

Oil	4500 Calories/pound
Coal	3600 Calories/pound
Wood	1800 Calories/pound
TNT	450 Calories/pound

We see from this listing that the expected factor of a million between the energy yields of nuclear and chemical reactions is achieved with something to spare. Since mining and transportation costs of fuels tend to be proportional to the amount of material needed, nuclear fuel has a great potential even in competition with coal or oil.

We have seen in Chapter VII that a low energy neutron is capable of producing fission in some nuclei (like U^{235}), the large energy output being achieved with virtually no energy input. Here, obviously, is a very favorable situation for energy production. Furthermore, several neutrons are emitted in the fission process, and these become available for inducing further fission reactions. Fission is therefore a net producer, rather than a consumer, of neutrons. To make matters even more favorable, the cross section for fission induced by thermal neutrons in U^{235} is rather large.

It would seem that to produce nuclear energy one need only introduce a few neutrons into a block of U^{235}; these will induce fission reactions, which will release neutrons, and those neutrons will induce further fissions, and so on. This process is called a *chain reaction*. It turns out, in fact, that even the introduction of neutrons is no problem; neutrons from cosmic rays are sufficient. However, there are a few catches and problems.

The first catch is in the fact that the block of U^{235}

bread or sugar (which are chemically similar to wood). Dieters may also be aware that to remove a pound of fat one must be deprived of about 4500 calories.

must be large enough to ensure that the neutrons will strike a nucleus before they escape from the material. This condition would not be difficult if it were not that U^{235} occurs in nature only as an 0.7 per cent constituent of ordinary uranium, the rest of which is U^{238}. We noted in Chapter VII that this U^{238} undergoes neutron capture, removing neutrons without replacing them. One must therefore pay a heavy price in other factors in order to start a chain reaction with ordinary uranium. It is very much easier if the U^{238} is removed and only the U^{235} is used. Separation of these two uranium isotopes is a very difficult and expensive undertaking. It was the major item in the atomic bomb project of World War II. While it is now done on a large scale and relatively cheaply (about $5000 per pound for 90 per cent U^{235}) in the United States, the process is sufficiently intricate that most other countries still have not mastered it.

The second catch in our simple-minded proposal for obtaining nuclear energy is that the neutrons emitted in fission (Chapter VI) have energies of the order of MeV, while the cross section for neutron-induced fission becomes large only at very low energies, of the order of eV. This problem can be overcome by introducing a *moderator*; that is, a material in which neutrons lose energy by collision without being captured. Such a material must have a very low cross section for neutron capture and, in addition, must be relatively light in atomic weight. The latter requirement arises because particles do not lose much energy in a collision with objects of very different mass. A tennis ball striking a bowling ball bounces off with little loss of energy, but if it strikes another tennis ball, the energy is, on the average, equally shared between the two. From this point of view, hydrogen would be an excellent moderator, but, unfortunately, it has an uncomfortably large cross section for neutron capture.

The next lightest material is deuterium (H^2), which does have a very small neutron-capture cross section. Deuterium is an ideal moderator and frequently is used in the form of *heavy water*, ($H^2)_2O$. (Oxygen, fortunately, also has a very small neutron-capture cross section.) The only drawback is that deuterium occurs in nature only as a small fraction (150 parts per million) of ordinary hydrogen, and separating the two is a somewhat expensive process (several hundred dollars per pound of deuterium). Other materials of low atomic weight (carbon or beryllium, for example) are sometimes used, and occasionally ordinary water is used in spite of the troublesome neutron-capture cross section of ordinary hydrogen.

Another problem in producing nuclear energy is that the reaction rate must be controlled; it must be kept sufficiently slow that the heat can be removed without melting the materials or causing an explosion. One way of controlling the reaction rate is to introduce a rod of a material with a high neutron-capture cross section, such as cadmium. Pushing the rod into the reactor reduces the number of neutrons available for fission and thus slows the reaction rate; conversely, pulling it out accelerates the reaction rate.

The hazards of radiation must be guarded against. Fission fragments, being highly excited nuclei, decay first by neutron emission, but when sufficient energy for this is no longer available, decay to their normal states by successive gamma-ray emission. Since neutrons and gamma rays are not easily stopped, a goodly number escape out the sides of the reactor. Reactors must therefore be shielded with thick concrete walls.

In essentially all cases, the fission fragments are unstable in respect to beta decay. For example, the stable nucleus of mass 119 is $\boxed{50 \mid 69 \mid \text{Sn-119}}$; the nucleus $\boxed{46 \mid 73 \mid \text{Pd-119}}$ released in Equation (2) of Chapter IV must eventually decay into the stable nucleus. It first decays to $\boxed{47 \mid 72 \mid \text{Ag-119}}$, which then decays to $\boxed{48 \mid 71 \mid \text{Cd-119}}$, which in turn decays to $\boxed{49 \mid 70 \mid \text{In-119}}$, which finally decays to $\boxed{50 \mid 69 \mid \text{Sn-119}}$. In each decay one neutron changes into a proton in accordance with the rules for the beta decay process. Most of these beta decays are accompanied by gamma-ray emission, and many of them have half-lives of many years. Consequently, the "ashes" of nuclear burning are highly radioactive. The ashes present a waste disposal problem that will eventually become crucial if much of the world's power is to be produced by fission. When this material is buried, great care must be taken lest it contaminate the ground water. If it were dumped into the sea, it would harm the fish and people who eat them.

Of course, there are engineering and economic problems associated with any practical device for production of nuclear power, but we will not deal with them here. After two decades of intensive study and experiment, nuclear power stations capable of competing economically with conventional power plants under some conditions are a reality.

Other nuclei besides $\boxed{92 \mid 143 \mid \text{U-235}}$ undergo fission when struck by low energy neutrons, the most important being $\boxed{94 \mid 145 \mid \text{Pu-239}}$ (Pu is the symbol for plutonium) and $\boxed{92 \mid 141 \mid \text{U-233}}$. Either of these can be used as reactor fuel or bomb material—actually, Pu^{239} has been used for bombs. The principal problem is that neither isotope occurs naturally; they must be produced artificially in nuclear reactors.

Plutonium is produced in the following sequence: a neutron-capture reaction on $\boxed{92\,|\,146\,|\,\text{U-238}}$ gives $\boxed{92\,|\,147\,|\,\text{U-239}}$ (the nucleus with one more neutron), which then goes by beta decay to $\boxed{93\,|\,146\,|\,\text{Np-239}}$, which beta-decays into $\boxed{94\,|\,145\,|\,\text{Pu-239}}$. For U^{233} the sequence is: $\boxed{90\,|\,142\,|\,\text{Th-232}}$ undergoes neutron capture to become $\boxed{90\,|\,143\,|\,\text{Th-233}}$, which then beta-decays to $\boxed{91\,|\,142\,|\,\text{Pa-233}}$, which beta-decays to $\boxed{92\,|\,141\,|\,\text{U-233}}$. In both cases, the starting materials are commonly available as natural uranium (99.3 per cent U^{238}) and natural thorium (100 per cent Th^{232}). They need only be left in a reactor for a period of time to absorb neutrons, and then chemically processed to yield the product. Of course, their effect in absorbing neutrons must be taken into account in the reactor operation. A neutron that is used to produce Pu^{239} or U^{233} is not available to produce energy by a fission process.

Power from Fusion

In the introduction to Chapter VI there was some discussion of *thermonuclear* reactions; that is, reactions among nuclei in which their electrical repulsion is overcome by their thermal energy at temperatures of 100 million degrees or more. Some of these reactions which give an energy output are:

$$\boxed{1\,|\,1\,|\,\text{H-2}} + \boxed{1\,|\,1\,|\,\text{H-2}} \rightarrow \boxed{2\,|\,1\,|\,\text{He-3}} + n + \ 3.3 \text{ MeV}$$

$$\boxed{1\,|\,1\,|\,\text{H-2}} + \boxed{1\,|\,1\,|\,\text{H-2}} \rightarrow \boxed{1\,|\,2\,|\,\text{H-3}} + p + \ 4.0 \text{ MeV}$$

$$\boxed{1\,|\,1\,|\,\text{H-2}} + \boxed{1\,|\,2\,|\,\text{H-3}} \rightarrow \boxed{2\,|\,2\,|\,\text{He-4}} + n + 17.6 \text{ MeV}$$

We will refer to them as "the thermonuclear energy reactions." The reacting nuclei (those on the left side)

are all hydrogen isotopes, $\boxed{1\,|\,1\,|\,\text{H-2}}$, which is usu-
ally called deuterium, and $\boxed{1\,|\,2\,|\,\text{H-3}}$, generally
known as tritium. The energies on the right side are
energies released in the reactions. We see that the
first two reactions release about 3.6 MeV per 4 mass
units of fuel, whereas fission releases 190 MeV per 235
mass units, or about 10 per cent less per unit mass.
The third reaction releases about five times as much
energy per pound as fission. Moreover, the raw materials for at least the first two of these reactions are
abundantly available in nature; 1 part in 7000 of ordinary hydrogen is deuterium, and the abundance of
hydrogen as the principal constituent of water is obvious. The tritium in the third reaction must be produced by neutron capture (Chapter VII) in nuclear
reactors, similarly to the production of Pu^{239} and
U^{233}, but hopefully it would be needed only to start
the reaction. Furthermore, the neutrons escaping from
the first reaction, as well as from the third reaction,
could be used to produce the tritium.

If we wanted to be flippant, we might say that to
make a thermonuclear reactor we need only to heat
up a bottle of deuterium to 100 million degrees and
drain off the energy. The problem, of course, is to
make the bottle. Clearly, at such temperatures no material bottle would do. The idea has been to design
a magnetic field that would contain the deuterium, a
sort of invisible "bottle." Some such apparatus does
seem possible. At those temperatures the orbital electron is not attached to the deuterium nucleus, which
therefore is electrically charged. It is a well-established
fact that individual charged particles can be contained
easily by magnetic fields. The problem is that the effects of collisions become very important in the sta-
bility of the containment. On the average, a deute-

rium nucleus must undergo thousands of collisions before participating in one of the energy-producing reactions. The cross sections for other collisions are that much larger than the cross sections for the thermonuclear energy reactions.

A dense conglomeration of electrically charged particles of both signs, the deuterium nuclei and electrons, is known as a *plasma*. To date, no one has been able to contain a plasma with magnetic fields for longer than a fraction of a second. If a stable magnetic bottle could be obtained, the many other problems to be faced would seem much less formidable. While the future of thermonuclear power on Earth is hedged with question marks, it seems reasonable to assume that someday, somehow, the problems will be solved and man will be able to produce energy by burning the deuterium that is so abundant in the seas.

Bombs

In principle, an atomic bomb resembles a fission reactor. It consists of a quantity of U^{235} or some other fissionable material, and moderators. The control problem is completely different in the bomb because all the U^{235} must be consumed in fission within a very short time or it would be blown apart into pieces so small that the chain reaction would stop as neutrons escaped. This very fast burning is achieved by *implosion;* to start the process the pieces of fissionable material are blasted together with chemical explosives.

The power of bombs is expressed as the equivalent amount of TNT that by chemical explosion will produce the same energy. We have seen that fission of U^{235} releases 8 billion Calories per pound, as compared to 450 Calories per pound for TNT; accordingly, the energy release per unit weight is eighteen million times greater. A 1-megaton bomb (as the name implies) releases as much energy as 1 million tons—2 billion pounds—of TNT. About 110 pounds of U^{235} (that is, 2 billion pounds divided by 18 million) must be burned. The bombs dropped on Japan had a power of about 25 kilotons, or forty times less; they required the burning of only about 3 pounds of fissionable material.

Fission fragments, as we have said, are generally radioactive; they go through a series of beta decays followed, in many cases, by gamma-ray emission. Due to the presence of this radioactive material, the area surrounding the explosion becomes uninhabitable for some time. Worse still, some of the radioactive material rises high into the atmosphere where it is carried long distances on the wind before it comes down as *radioactive fallout*. It is to avoid these radiation hazards that the nations of the world have sought a workable nuclear test ban.

The nucleus of cobalt has a relatively large cross section for the neutron-capture reaction $\boxed{27\,|\,32\,|\,\text{Co-59}}$ (n,γ) $\boxed{27\,|\,33\,|\,\text{Co-60}}$. The isotope produced, Co^{60}, beta-decays with a half-life of five years, accompanied by the emission of high energy gamma rays. Thus, if cobalt is added to a fission bomb, it would capture many of the neutrons to produce large quantities of Co^{60}, which would be added to the fallout. The fallout would become many times more hazardous, and perhaps would make vast areas of the Earth uninhabitable for many years. This device, which could be made with very little difficulty by any nation possessing atomic bombs, is known as the "cobalt bomb."

The hydrogen bomb depends on the thermonuclear energy reactions between deuterium and tritium (which are isotopes of hydrogen—hence the name). This is one type of thermonuclear reaction in which a bottle for containment is not a problem. All the material is consumed in too short a time for it to escape. The thermonuclear temperature, hundreds of millions of degrees, is obtained from the explosion of a fission bomb, referred to as the *trigger*, which is part of the device. We have seen that the reaction between deuterium and tritium releases five times as much energy per unit weight as does a fission bomb; a 1-megaton hydrogen bomb could thus burn as little as 22 pounds of material ($\frac{1}{5}$ of the 110 pounds mentioned). A 100-megaton bomb, which the Russians claim to have developed, must burn more than 2000 pounds.

None of the products of the thermonuclear energy reactions, He^3 or He^4, is radioactive. (The tritium produced in the second reaction is slightly radioactive, but it is rapidly consumed in the third reaction.) A hydrogen bomb thus does not produce fallout or local radiation hazards, except for those caused by the fission trigger bomb. Bombs requiring relatively small triggers are therefore referred to as "clean," while "dirty" bombs have large triggers and thereby produce a great deal of radioactivity.

There has been some talk of attaining in chemical explosions the temperatures needed for thermonuclear reactions. This arrangement would eliminate the need for fission bomb triggering, and all but eliminate radioactivity. The bomb might kill all the inhabitants with the neutrons it produces, but an invading army could still occupy the area without fear of being injured by radiation. This device is referred to as a "neutron bomb."

For all the terrible effects of nuclear bombs, and

despite the vast potential of nuclear energy as a source of power, however, the truly tremendous nuclear processes are those found not on Earth but in stars. A discussion of these and of their significance in the creation of the universe will provide the climax for this book.

CHAPTER X

NUCLEAR ENERGY—IN THE STARS

Great difficulties confront us in our attempts to maintain on Earth the temperatures at which thermonuclear reactions can occur, but such conditions arise naturally in stars as large as our Sun. Stars form from gases which, under gravitational forces, contract into fairly dense spheres. As gravitational forces pull in the gas atoms, they accelerate them, just as gravity accelerates bodies falling toward the Earth. In any gas the average speed of the atoms determines the temperature. So it is that in the "falling" of gas atoms toward the centers of stars the temperature of the gas increases. The mass of our Sun is so great, and consequently the gravitational forces are so large, that by the time gas has contracted to the size of the Sun, the temperature at the center has reached about 10 million degrees.* The atoms are so tightly packed together from the crushing force of so vast an amount of material pushing in on them that the density is about 3 pounds per cubic inch, ten times the density

* Temperatures used here are on the centigrade scale. To convert to Fahrenheit temperature, multiply by 1.8.

of lead. Under these conditions *hydrogen burning* occurs.*

Hydrogen burning refers to the thermonuclear process in which protons undergo a series of reactions resulting in the formation of He^4 from four protons. Because of the relatively small electrical repulsion (Chapter VII), hydrogen nuclei undergo thermonuclear reactions more readily than any other element. Since more than 90 per cent of all the nuclei in the universe are hydrogen,† these processes dominate the generation of energy in stars. There are two such processes, known as the *proton-proton chain* and the *carbon cycle.*

The proton-proton chain consists of the following series of reactions and decays:

$$H^1 + H^1 \rightarrow He^2$$
$$He^2 \rightarrow \beta + H^2$$
$$H^2 + H^1 \rightarrow He^3 + \gamma$$

either   or

$$He^3(\alpha,\gamma)Be^7 \qquad\qquad He^3(He^3,2p)He^4$$
$$Be^7 \rightarrow \beta + Li^7$$
$$Li^7(p,\alpha)He^4$$

Let us now explain the various steps in detail. The chain begins with a collision of two protons to form the nucleus $\boxed{2 \mid 0 \mid \text{He-2}}$. This nucleus, being unstable, breaks up into two protons (this is an example of nucleon decay) with a half-life of about 10^{-22} second; however, it also can decay by beta decay into $\boxed{1 \mid 1 \mid \text{H-2}}$ (deuterium) with a half-life of about

* The thermonuclear energy reactions listed in the last chapter occur before this, but since there is relatively little deuterium available in stars, they are not significant.

† About 9 per cent are helium, and about 0.1 per cent other elements.

10,000 seconds. The probability per second for nucleon decay is thus about 10^{26} times greater than for beta decay. Only once in 10^{26} reactions is a deuterium nucleus formed. These events are so rare that the chance of a given proton participating is only 1 in 10 billion per year; but there are so many protons in the Sun that deuterium is produced in these reactions at a rate of 10 billion tons per second.

Once deuterium nuclei are formed, they very rapidly undergo (p,γ) reactions to form $\boxed{2\ |\ 1\ |\ \text{He-3}}$; the average life of a deuterium nucleus in the center of the Sun before undergoing this reaction is about 2 seconds. Once He^3 is formed, the rest of the chain usually proceeds in one of two ways. If there is a reasonable amount of He^4 available,* as in the Sun, there can be (He^3,γ) reactions on it to produce $\boxed{4\ |\ 3\ |\ \text{Be-7}}$; that is, an He^3 and an He^4 nucleus collide to form a highly excited state (compound nucleus) of Be^7, which then decays by gamma-ray emission to the normal state of Be^7. The Be^7 then beta-decays† to Li^7, which then is rapidly consumed in a (p,α) reaction, leaving another alpha particle as residue. The net effect of this chain is that one alpha particle and four protons have reacted and, at the end, two alpha particles have been released. In effect, four protons have fused to form an alpha particle. The binding energy of the alpha particle—28 MeV accord-

---

* We use the names He^4 and alpha particle (α) interchangeably; they are two names for the same nucleus. Similarly, for H^1 and the proton, and for other atoms and their nuclei.

† This is a type of beta decay we have not mentioned previously. Instead of emitting a positive electron, the Be^7 nucleus captures a negative electron, simultaneously emitting a neutrino.

ing to Fig. 5—is released as kinetic energy of the various emerging particles and gamma rays.

If there is not much He^4 available when the He^3 is formed, two He^3 nuclei eventually collide in a $He^3(He^3,2p)He^4$ reaction. Once again, the effect of the chain is to fuse four protons to produce one He^4 nucleus. The energy release is again about 28 MeV.

These proton-proton chains account for the energy radiated by our Sun. The rate at which they proceed is determined by the slowest link in the chain, the formation of deuterium from proton-proton collisions. At this rate all the hydrogen in the Sun would be consumed in about 10 billion years. Fortunately for us, the Sun is only about 5 billion years old, so it should continue to pour out energy at about the present rate for another 5 billion years.

In some stars, the most important process for energy production is the carbon cycle, which consists principally of the chain:

$$C^{12}(p,\gamma)N^{13}$$
$$N^{13} \rightarrow \beta + C^{13}$$
$$C^{13}(p,\gamma)N^{14}$$
$$N^{14}(p,\gamma)O^{15}$$
$$O^{15} \rightarrow \beta + N^{15}$$
$$N^{15}(p,\alpha)C^{12}$$

It starts with a (p,γ) reaction on $\boxed{6 \mid 6 \mid C\text{-}12}$, leading to $\boxed{7 \mid 6 \mid N\text{-}13}$, which then beta-decays to $\boxed{6 \mid 7 \mid C\text{-}13}$. This last undergoes a (p,γ) reaction leading to $\boxed{7 \mid 7 \mid N\text{-}14}$, which undergoes another (p,γ) reaction leading to $\boxed{8 \mid 7 \mid O\text{-}15}$. This oxygen isotope beta-decays, with a half-life of only two minutes, to $\boxed{7 \mid 8 \mid N\text{-}15}$, which undergoes a (p,α) reaction, leaving $\boxed{6 \mid 6 \mid C\text{-}12}$ as the residual nucleus. The net effect of the cycle is that four protons have been consumed and an alpha particle produced. Again about 28 MeV of energy has been released. Note that C^{12} is not consumed; the initial C^{12} nucleus is replaced at the end of the cycle by another C^{12} nucleus.

The carbon cycle requires a higher temperature than the proton-proton chain since the nuclei involved in the former have more protons and hence create a stronger electrical repulsion to be overcome. This cycle also requires that an appreciable quantity of carbon be present, typically about 1 per cent. On the other hand, there is no reaction involved that is inherently as slow as the first step in the proton-proton chain. In stars just slightly hotter than the Sun, the carbon cycle is often the predominant process.

The temperature of a star depends on the strength of the gravitational forces accelerating the atoms and causing them to fall toward the center. Since the gravitational forces depend on the amount of mass present, stars of greater mass have higher temperature. It is therefore in stars larger than our Sun that energy is produced by the carbon cycle.

Whether the hydrogen is burned by the proton-proton chain or by the carbon cycle, it eventually is used up, leaving the star with a core of helium, product of the burning process. Helium does not burn easily because a collision between two alpha particles (that is, helium nuclei) leads to $\boxed{4 \mid 4 \mid \text{Be-8}}$, which, with half-life of 3×10^{-16} second, decays back to two alpha particles (this is an example of alpha decay). Even if a third alpha particle should strike before the Be^8 nucleus decays, the nucleus formed is $\boxed{6 \mid 6 \mid \text{C-12}}$ in an excited state, which 99.9 per cent of the time decays back to three alpha particles.

In the other 0.1 per cent of the time the excited state of C^{12} decays by successive gamma-ray emissions to the normal state of C^{12}. It is only in this fantastically unlikely situation that helium nuclei can participate in energy-producing reactions. Because it is so improbable, this reaction—known as *helium burning*—does not occur with appreciable frequency until the temperature reaches 100 million degrees and the atoms are so tightly pressed together that the density becomes 10,000 times the density of lead, about 1 ton per cubic inch! Let us see how such conditions are achieved.

Once the hydrogen has been consumed, no further nuclear reactions can occur. The star begins to contract under gravitational forces—atoms fall with increasing velocity (and therefore temperature) toward the center, causing the density of the core to increase. During this process, the structure of the star undergoes tremendous change. The outer envelope of the star expands by a large factor, changing the star into what is known to astronomers as a *red giant*. When this happens to our Sun (in about 5 billion years) it will expand so much that its outer layers will encompass the planet Mercury, and perhaps also Venus and the Earth. The star in this stage often spews vast amounts of material into interstellar space, and it is partly from this gas that new stars are formed. (Other known sources of interstellar gas are novae and supernovae explosions, rare but fantastically powerful events that stir the imagination of everyone interested in astronomy.)

When the temperature and density of the core have reached 100 million degrees and 1 ton per cubic inch, respectively, helium burning commences, leading to two important effects: the temperature rises further from the energy release of the reaction, and the product of helium burning, C^{12}, is formed in large quantities. A number of other interesting reactions then become possible, leading to formation of many other nuclei which can in turn participate in further reactions.

CHAPTER XI

ORIGIN OF THE ELEMENTS

The origin of the universe is, and will remain, a mystery, but it seems likely that matter first appeared as electrons and protons. The protons combined in various nuclear reactions, some of which we have discussed, to form all the nuclei found in nature, with proton numbers roughly spanning the range from one to a hundred. Once in relatively cool environments, the protons captured, by electrical force, a number of electrons equal to the number of protons, and became electrically neutral atoms. These are the atoms of the chemical elements. The chemical properties of atoms (and indeed virtually all the properties of matter on the Earth) arise from the arrangements of electrons, the number of which determines the structure. But this number is determined by the nucleus. So, in a very real sense, a chemical element is created when its nucleus is formed. It is the formation of these nuclei that we will discuss in this chapter.

But first we perhaps should clarify some ideas about thermonuclear reactions that we already have been using and will use further here. In determining the probability that a collision will result in a nuclear reaction two factors are most important, the barrier penetration and the temperature. The barrier penetration determines how often the two colliding particles get close enough together for nuclear forces to come into play and cause a reaction. The temperature determines the probability that the colliding particles will have enough energy to penetrate the barrier.

Particles participating in thermonuclear reactions have energies far below the barrier. For example, a typical alpha particle in a red-giant star would participate in a helium-burning reaction (to form C^{12}) in about a millionth of a second if it were not for the barrier. As things are, the average time required is about a billion years; so the barrier penetration has reduced the reaction rate by a factor of about 10^{22}. When energies are so far below the barrier, the barrier penetration increases very rapidly with increasing particle energy. Examples of this from alpha decay were given in Chapter VI. As another example more pertinent here, the barrier penetration for protons colliding with a $\boxed{3\ 4\ \text{Li-7}}$ nucleus—one of the reactions in the proton-proton chain—increases by a factor of 10^{30} from .001 to .01 MeV, by a factor of a million (10^6) from .01 to .1 MeV, and by a factor of 500 from .1 to 1 MeV.

The temperature of a gas, at earthly or stellar temperature, gives the average energy of the particles—one electron volt (eV) of energy for every 12,000 degrees of temperature. However, the energy of any one particle is subject to large fluctuations (the so-called *Maxwell distribution*) about that average. Well-known statistical treatments show that in a typical gas 1 particle in 7000 has 10 times the average energy; 1 in 50 million has 20 times, and 1 in 400 billion has 30 times the average.

Since the barrier penetration increases very rapidly with increasing energy, it is these particles of much higher than average energy that, in spite of their relatively small numbers, cause most of the reactions. The number of these particles with a given energy increases very rapidly with increasing temperature. For example, from the figures in the last paragraph we see that when a 50 per cent rise in temperature increases the average energy from 1000 to 1500 eV, it changes drastically the distribution of 30,000-eV particles. Instead of having 30 times the average energy, they have only 20 times, and their number consequently rises from 1 in 400 billion to 1 in 50 million, an increase by a factor of 7000. Thus the reaction rates increase very rapidly with increasing temperature; some examples are given in Table III. We can see also in Table III that reactions involving nuclei of higher atomic number require higher energies. Because there is more electrical repulsion between the reacting particles, a higher barrier must be overcome.

TABLE III

Relative Reaction Rates at Various Temperatures

Reaction	Relative Reaction Rates		
	20 million deg.	100 million deg.	500 million deg.
$p-$ $\boxed{1 \mid 1 \mid \text{H-2}}$	1	10	10
$p-$ $\boxed{6 \mid 6 \mid \text{C-12}}$	3×10^{-14}	1×10^{-7}	3×10^{-5}
$p-$ $\boxed{14 \mid 16 \mid \text{Si-30}}$	2×10^{-28}	4×10^{-15}	8×10^{-11}
$\alpha-$ $\boxed{6 \mid 6 \mid \text{C-12}}$	5×10^{-41}	8×10^{-21}	3×10^{-12}

Many factors of lesser importance contribute to reaction rates. A reaction may have a resonance in the energy region of interest; the most striking example is the $\text{Li}^7(p,\alpha)\text{He}^4$ reaction which terminates the proton-proton chain. This reaction has a very strong resonance which increases its reaction rate by a factor of 40,000 over the expected. Another factor is the density of particles; clearly, the reaction rate is proportional to it.

Now let us return to the point where we had helium burning to produce C^{12} at a temperature of 100 million degrees. As the temperature rises from this burning, other reactions become possible. For example $C^{12}(\alpha,\gamma)O^{16}$ and $O^{16}(\alpha,\gamma)Ne^{20}$ become important almost immediately; O^{16} and Ne^{20} are formed in appreciable quantities, and the energy release further raises the temperature. When the temperature reaches 600 million degrees, reactions between carbon nuclei begin to become important; some of these are $C^{12}(C^{12},\gamma)Mg^{24}$; $C^{12}(C^{12},p)Na^{23}$; $C^{12}(C^{12},n)Mg^{23}$. The protons released in the second reaction have an energy of more than 2 MeV and can easily react with any of the nuclei present to form nuclei of still higher atomic number.

If the temperature reaches 1.2 billion degrees, $Ne^{20}(\gamma,\alpha)O^{16}$ reactions occur. At 1.6 billion degrees, reactions between O^{16} nuclei become important, leading to much the same results as the reactions between C^{12} nuclei.

While it is difficult to keep up with the bookkeeping as elements are produced and sometimes destroyed in these processes, it is not difficult to understand why oxygen, neon, nitrogen, carbon, and silicon (in that order) are the most abundant elements in the universe after hydrogen and helium. Carbon, which is the direct result of helium burning, would be the most abundant of this group if it were not so frequently destroyed in subsequent reactions. The most prominent of these reactions lead to oxygen and neon—$\frac{1}{3000}$ of the nuclei in the universe are oxygen, and neon is about half that abundant. Carbon is only about $\frac{1}{6}$ as abundant as oxygen.

At higher and higher temperatures heavier and heavier nuclei are produced, but, on the other hand, they are sometimes destroyed, as we have seen in the case of carbon. As more of an element is produced, it is more frequently destroyed until an equilibrium is reached between production and destruction. If temperatures become high enough for complete equilibrium (about 4 billion degrees), the number of nuclei of each type present is determined by their binding energy—more strongly bound nuclei are more easily produced and less easily destroyed. From Fig. 5 we see that the maximum binding occurs in the region of atomic weight 56, which corresponds to iron. One in 100,000 atoms in the universe is iron, which is the eighth most abundant element. Only 1 nucleus in 100 million is of atomic weight greater than 70; 90 per cent of these are between 70 and 90.

So far we have ignored the effects of neutrons. Many of the reactions we have been discussing such as (α,n), (C^{12},n) lead to production of neutrons. Electrical repulsion does not hinder them from entering nuclei; they reach thermal energies and are captured in about 10^{-10} second. The most probable reactions at this energy are (n,n) or (n,γ). If it is the former, the resulting neutron undergoes the same process, so that ultimately, almost all lead to (n,γ) reactions.[*]

An (n,γ) reaction leads to a nucleus with atomic weight increased by one. In the situations we are presently concerned with, the nucleus will beta-decay to the stable nucleus of that atomic weight. This nucleus may later capture an additional neutron, and eventually nuclei of a very high atomic weight are produced. The number of nuclei with a given atomic weight is inversely proportional to the neutron-capture cross section, since a nucleus with a small cross section is not easily destroyed by a later capture.

This process explains the formation of the heavy

[*] The (n,p) reaction, especially in N^{14}, is an exception to this rule. In some cases, it absorbs so many neutrons that it excludes the processes we are discussing.

elements up to $\boxed{83 \mid 126 \mid \text{Bi-209}}$, but it cannot explain the existence of heavier elements, which decay by alpha-particle emission and therefore lose atomic weight. The very heavy elements, such as thorium and uranium, are formed in supernovae, the powerful stellar explosions in which nuclear reactions occur at a tremendous rate. Neutrons are produced so rapidly that a nucleus typically captures one every second or so. Under these conditions, the nuclei usually do not have time to decay by beta or alpha emission before the next neutron capture occurs. This process accounts also for the production of some of the neutron-rich isotopes of lighter mass, but in these cases only isotopes with very small neutron-capture cross sections can survive.

Some formation of elements goes on in the outer regions of stars; otherwise the existence of deuterium, lithium, beryllium, and boron would be hard to explain. They are produced in great abundance in the interiors of stars, but there they are rapidly destroyed in further nuclear reactions. For example, we have said that deuterium lasts only for about two seconds near the center of the Sun. Similarly, $\boxed{3 \mid 3 \mid \text{Li-6}}$ lasts for five seconds, $\boxed{3 \mid 4 \mid \text{Li-7}}$ for one minute. In the outer regions of stars or in surface disturbances, thermonuclear reactions occur much less rapidly, or in very short bursts, so that these nuclei can be made with some probability of survival.

So, we are justified in describing the stars, our Sun among them, as gigantic thermonuclear reactors, furnaces where nuclei are burned in nuclear reactions much as gas or coal is burned in chemical reactions in our home furnaces. From this burning comes, directly or indirectly, essentially all the energy in the universe, and all matter in all its forms except the proton and the electron.

TABLE OF ELEMENTS

Atomic Number	Element	Symbol	Most Common Nucleus
1	Hydrogen	H	1 | 0 | H-1
2	Helium	He	2 | 2 | He-4
3	Lithium	Li	3 | 4 | Li-7
4	Beryllium	Be	4 | 5 | Be-9
5	Boron	B	5 | 6 | B-11
6	Carbon	C	6 | 6 | C-12
7	Nitrogen	N	7 | 7 | N-14
8	Oxygen	O	8 | 8 | O-16
9	Fluorine	F	9 | 10 | F-19
10	Neon	Ne	10 | 10 | Ne-20
11	Sodium	Na	11 | 12 | Na-23
12	Magnesium	Mg	12 | 12 | Mg-24
13	Aluminum	Al	13 | 14 | Al-27
14	Silicon	Si	14 | 14 | Si-28
15	Phosphorus	P	15 | 16 | P-31
16	Sulfur	S	16 | 16 | S-32
17	Chlorine	Cl	17 | 18 | Cl-35

Atomic Number	Element	Symbol	Most Common Nucleus
18	Argon	Ar	18 | 22 | Ar-40
19	Potassium	K	19 | 20 | K-39
20	Calcium	Ca	20 | 20 | Ca-40
21	Scandium	Sc	21 | 24 | Sc-45
22	Titanium	Ti	22 | 26 | Ti-48
23	Vanadium	V	23 | 28 | V-51
24	Chromium	Cr	24 | 28 | Cr-52
25	Manganese	Mn	25 | 30 | Mn-55
26	Iron	Fe	26 | 30 | Fe-56
27	Cobalt	Co	27 | 32 | Co-59
28	Nickel	Ni	28 | 30 | Ni-58
29	Copper	Cu	29 | 34 | Cu-63
30	Zinc	Zn	30 | 34 | Zn-64
31	Gallium	Ga	31 | 38 | Ga-69
32	Germanium	Ge	32 | 42 | Ge-74
33	Arsenic	As	33 | 42 | As-75
34	Selenium	Se	34 | 46 | Se-80
35	Bromine	Br	35 | 44 | Br-79
36	Krypton	Kr	36 | 48 | Kr-84
37	Rubidium	Rb	37 | 48 | Rb-85
38	Strontium	Sr	38 | 50 | Sr-88
39	Yttrium	Y	39 | 50 | Y-89
40	Zirconium	Zr	40 | 50 | Zr-90
41	Niobium	Nb	41 | 52 | Nb-93

42	Molybdenum	Mo	42	56	Mo-98
43	Technetium	Tc	43	56	Tc-99
44	Ruthenium	Ru	44	58	Ru-102
45	Rhodium	Rh	45	58	Rh-103
46	Palladium	Pd	46	60	Pd-106
47	Silver	Ag	47	60	Ag-107
48	Cadmium	Cd	48	66	Cd-114
49	Indium	In	49	66	In-115
50	Tin	Sn	50	67	Sn-120
51	Antimony	Sb	51	70	Sb-121
52	Tellurium	Te	52	78	Te-130
53	Iodine	I	53	74	I-127
54	Xenon	Xe	54	78	Xe-132
55	Cesium	Cs	55	78	Cs-133
56	Barium	Ba	56	82	Ba-138
57	Lanthanum	La	57	82	La-139
58	Cerium	Ce	58	82	Ce-140
59	Praseodymium	Pr	59	82	Pr-141
60	Neodymium	Nd	60	82	Nd-142
61	Promethium	Pm	61	86	Pm-147
62	Samarium	Sm	62	90	Sm-152
63	Europium	Eu	63	90	Eu-153
64	Gadolinium	Gd	64	94	Gd-158
65	Terbium	Tb	65	94	Tb-159
66	Dysprosium	Dy	66	96	Dy-162
67	Holmium	Ho	67	98	Ho-165
68	Erbium	Er	68	100	Er-168

Atomic Number	Element	Symbol	Most Common Nucleus
69	Thulium	Tm	69 | 100 | Tm-169
70	Ytterbium	Yb	70 | 104 | Yb-174
71	Lutecium	Lu	71 | 104 | Lu-175
72	Hafnium	Hf	72 | 108 | Hf-180
73	Tantalum	Ta	73 | 108 | Ta-181
74	Tungsten	W	74 | 110 | W-184
75	Rhenium	Re	75 | 112 | Re-187
76	Osmium	Os	76 | 116 | Os-192
77	Iridium	Ir	77 | 116 | Ir-193
78	Platinum	Pt	78 | 117 | Pt-195
79	Gold	Au	79 | 118 | Au-197
80	Mercury	Hg	80 | 122 | Hg-202
81	Thallium	Tl	81 | 124 | Tl-205
82	Lead	Pb	82 | 126 | Pb-208
83	Bismuth	Bi	83 | 126 | Bi-209
84	Polonium	Po	84 | 126 | Po-210
85	Astatine	At	85 | 128 | At-213
86	Radon	Rn	86 | 136 | Rn-222
87	Francium	Fr	87 | 136 | Fr-223
88	Radium	Ra	88 | 138 | Ra-226
89	Actinium	Ac	89 | 138 | Ac-227
90	Thorium	Th	90 | 142 | Th-232
91	Protactinium	Pa	91 | 140 | Pa-231
92	Uranium	U	92 | 146 | U-238
93	Neptunium	Np	93 | 144 | Np-237

94	Plutonium	Pu	94 | 148 | Pu-238
95	Americium	Am	95 | 148 | Am-243
96	Curium	Cm	96 | 149 | Cm-245
97	Berkelium	Bk	97 | 152 | Bk-249
98	Californium	Cf	98 | 151 | Cf-249
99	Einsteinium	Es	99 | 154 | Es-253
100	Fermium	Fm	100 | 155 | Fm-255
101	Mendelevium	Md	101 | 155 | Md-256
102	Nobelium	No	102 | 151 | No-253
103	Lawrencium	Lw	103 | 154 | Lw-257

INDEX